A NATURAL HISTORY of Camden and Rockport

by E. C. Parker

published by

The Camden-Rockport Historical Society

"A Natural History of Camden and Rockport"

by E. C. Parker

The Camden-Rockport Historical Society
Box 897, Camden, Me. 04843

~

E.C. Parker
68 Washington St.
Camden, Me.
04843

2nd printing 1999

ISBN 0-9669907-0-6

Camden-Rockport Historical Society
Camden, Maine 04843

September 1984

The Camden-Rockport Historical Society is privileged and proud to publish this unique and engaging Natural History of Camden and Rockport by Elizabeth Parker.

This book is not only natural history, but cultural history as well. It is history at its best - history which tells us where we are in time and place - which gives us a sense of partnership with this small reach of the universe and, hopefully, a sense of stewardship for its future.

Many pleasant hours of thought-provoking discovery await the reader and user of this information-packed volume.

James Perry
James Perry
President

Foreword

by Lew Dietz

Few Maine towns lack a local history, annals which tell the present how it was in the past and chronicle the happenings which shaped the destiny of a community. Such histories tell the village inhabitants who they are and from whence they came. The Maine native who is inclined to take for granted the natural world around him does so at his peril, for the land rather than the people who settled upon it is his prime and precious heritage.

There was a time in Maine's early history when man's battle was against nature. The "howling wilderness" was the dark enemy to be subdued. Today we have come to the belated realization that, if we are to survive, we must side with nature. Thoreau wrote, "Strange that so few ever come to the woods to see how the pine tree lives and grows and spires, lifting its evergreen arms to the light, to see perfect success; but most are content to behold it in the shape of so many board feet and deem that its true success."

E.C. (Beedy) Parker has written, or, perhaps more accurately, gathered together a natural history of a special region to remind us of the primacy of the land and to instruct us in understanding the wonders of this special environment. Call it a natural history primer, for it is designed to serve the old and the young alike as a guide to a deeper appreciation of this small place those of us who reside here call home.

Lew Dietz
Rockport Sept 1984

INTRODUCTION

In this place, under low mountains on the shore of a bay of the Atlantic Ocean, there is an enormous variety of plant and animal life. The animals and plants of the area are presented here as they appear in the particular places - habitats - in which they are usually found. Each habitat has its typical range of temperature, humidity and availability of nutrients. Accordingly, certain plants & animals are able to live in interdependence in each habitat. On this matrix of the living and non-living, our human species exists. Our past, present & future lives are strongly influenced by our environment and we, in turn, have a significant impact on our surroundings, often unintentional. In particular, the observer should note the richness of life at the water's edge, both fresh and salt. The great mass of plant & animal material comes from these zones, water being the medium that most easily transports nutrients. These areas are most vulnerable to human business and also most difficult for us to observe, understand and appreciate. The soils of an area are also a delicate medium of transmission of nutrients that is often overlooked & taken for granted by humanity. By using this guide, the observer should be able to know what to look for in a particular habitat - in the woods, by the shore, on the mountain. I hope that a natural history will prove useful to all people making use of this land: students, householders, sportspeople, builders, administrators and visitors. Perhaps people in other areas will be inspired to make similar natural guides for their home lands.

CONTENTS

I would like to thank the people who helped to answer my questions about the natural history and history of Camden & Rockport: George Rossbach Neil Hotchkiss, Earl Kelly, Dorothy Spaulding, Marty Lunn, Mr. & Mrs. Richard Claybourne, Porge Buck, Julia Moore, Una Ames, Luke Sunde George Stevenson, Taylor Mudge, Bob Graham, Ted Brown, Bob Knight, Phil Marcoux, Laurence Nash, Bart Cadbury, Perry Shegarian, Beth Miller, Ellen Marckoon, Bill Gribbel, Erland Quinn, Paula LaVoie, Havilah Hawkins, Sr., Tony Oppensdorf, Ernest Maxcy, Rob Lovell, David Ridley and Jim Martin.

I wish to thank the Camden-Rockport Historical Society for making this publication possible, and Tom Marx and the Camden-Rockport school system for encouragement and support.

For their kind readings and criticisms, I am grateful to: George Rossbach, Meredith Martin, Lew Dietz and Richard Parker. I apologize for errors of omission and commission and hope the reader will let me know what corrections should be made.

Elizabeth C. Parker

Camden, 1984

WEATHER

The climate, where we live on the west side of the Penobscot bay (Latitude 44°12, Longitude 69°04'), is moderated by the ocean. It is damp, cool and temperate, as demonstrated by the following statistics:

Average annual temperature - 46°F.
average winter temperature - 24°F (10-20 days below zero/year)
average summer temperature - 66° F.
average annual precipitation - 47" wettest month: November 6" average rainfall
driest month: August: less than 3" average rainfall
average annual snowfall: 58" (equivalent of 5.8" of rain)

Number of clear days: 100-140
Number of days with snow on the ground: 40-80
average relative humidity in July at noon: over 70%
Frost free days (for warm weather crops) 115 growing days average
from April 26 - May 24 (last 32° frost) to Sept. 16 - Oct 14 (first 32° frost)
Cool weather crop growing days 200+
from March 29 - April 26 (last killing frost, 24°) to Oct 15 - Nov. 12 (first killing frost)
Heating degree days: 7700-8000 per year

Our weather comes mostly from the west. At our latitude (44°N.) the prevailing winds are westerly, as opposed to the easterly trade winds at 20° N. We often hear about weather systems approaching from the Midwest several days before they get to us. The islanders in the Bay to the east of us look west to Mt. Megunticook to see what their weather will be. If the sky sits low on the mountain, they know they will have rain.

Our large-scale weather is influenced by the

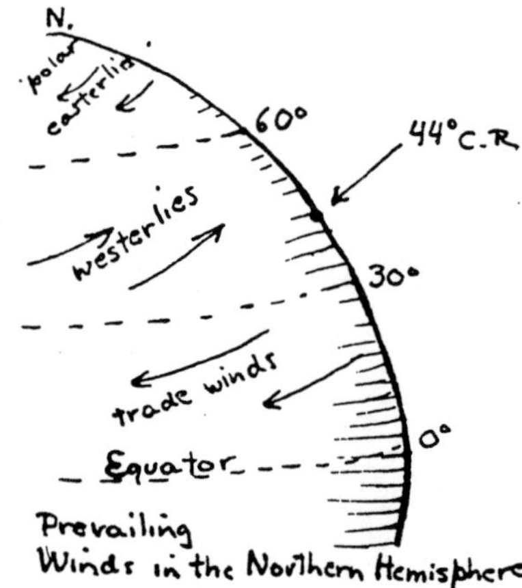

Prevailing Winds in the Northern Hemisphere

dry cold Continental Polar (cP) air masses in the winter and by warm moist Maritime Tropical (mT) air masses in the summer.

Continental Polar (cP) air mass, from N.W.

In the winter, the Camden Hills provide some shelter from the clear cold NW wind, but a careless sailor out of the harbor could be blown across the Bay. A more local winter phenomenon is the off-shore breeze that blows off the colder land, over the warmer sea. The sea, because it holds heat longer than the land, maintains a more even temperature year-round①, while the land cools and heats more quickly according to the weather (sun, air temperature, wind speed...) In the summer, in contrast, the afternoon breeze is off the sea, "on-shore" or "sea-breeze" - as the heating land sends the warmed air up and pulls in the cooler air off the water's surface. This breeze keeps us cool and comfortable on summer afternoons. The Camden Hills may exaggerate these off- and on-shore breezes, with their slope and heat mass.

mT

Maritime Tropical (mT) air mass from S.W.

cold land

warmer sea

Winter day

Land breeze

summer afternoon

warm land

cooler sea

Sea Breeze

Another winter phenomenon over the water is "sea-smoke" or "vapor": low streamers of steam rising vertically from the water surface on very cold, calm days, as the cold air condenses the water vapor lying over the warmer water surface.

There are several different kinds of mirages visible over the Bay. On still, clear days the islands seem to float above the surface of the water, "looming", as the light is bent by surface layers of air of different densities. Looming is considered to be a sign of changing weather, of an

① Sea water temperatures: Summer: 50-55°F near surface – in 40's below
Winter: Can be near freezing (or frozen) on surface (32°F) but in 40's just below.

"out wind" coming from the south the next day.

Icing is a problem in the winter for boats on the water in blowing winds. The spray can freeze in icy layers on the rigging and upper part of the boat, until the craft becomes unstable on rough seas.

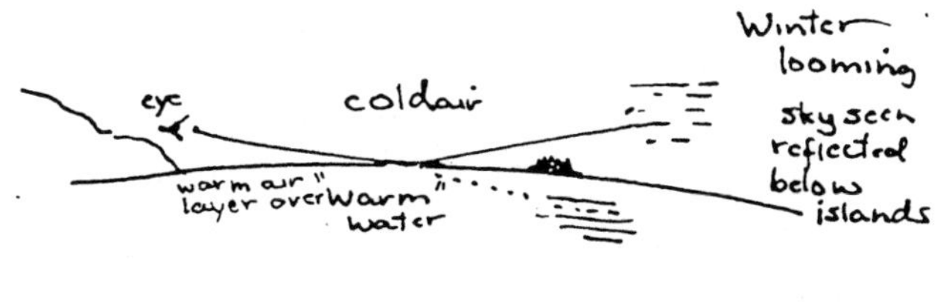

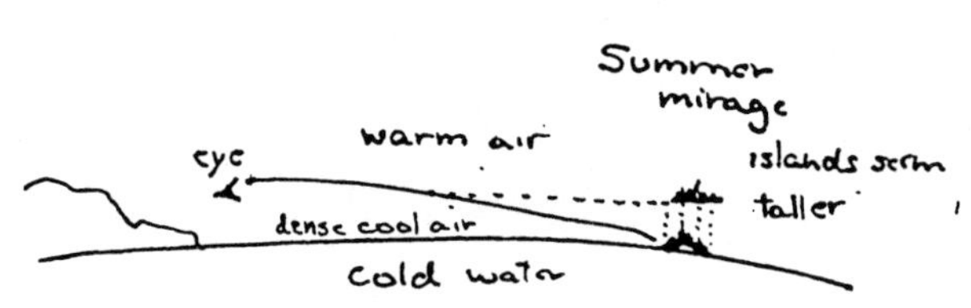

The harbors ice over sooner than the open shore, because of the fresh water coming in from the rivers has a higher freezing point than the saltier water off shore. Shore ice is heaved up by the tides and storm winds and damages waterfront structures. In 1868, 1877, 1904, 1918, 1923, 1933, 1947 parts of the bay froze over - and people could walk from the islands to the main.

On land, the moderate winter temperatures mean that there is much melting and refreezing of snow and ice. The snow cover often melts, to the distress of skiers, and road surfaces can be glazed with ice which requires careful driving.

Between winter and spring is the "mud season", about three weeks in March, when the ground thaws and refreezes. The sap rises in the trees on the warm days after the freezing nights. The surface layer of the ground thaws, but below is several feet of frozen earth. The wet surface cannot drain downwards and it must hold the moisture. It becomes jellylike or soupy when compressed by feet or vehicles. The "mud" only occurs where the ground cover is destroyed and we trample the soil. We cause it and are likewise inconvenienced by it.

Spring comes late along the coast. The inland gardens dry out and warm up much sooner than the coastal gardens. The cold water keeps the coastal land cool and foggy well into June. But by September the water in the bay has slowly warmed and it serves to keep the coast frost free during September and much of October, giving us a late growing season after the inland gardens have already had a "black frost".

WEATHER

In the summer, the south west winds predominate. This is the wind that sent sailing vessels "down east" along the coast, from Boston to Eastport and the Maritime Provinces. Sometimes the summer weather moves up from the south. The warm moist maritime air masses from the tropical Atlantic and the gulf of Mexico blow onto the cool gulf of Maine and hit the cold air over the Labrador Current that winds down from the north. Banks of fog build up over the Grand Banks and along the coast - and a south east wind can roll them up to the land. The weather often seems to form a line along the coast and to push back & forth so that no general weather forecast can be made as to whether it will be cloudy or sunny, wet or dry. This effect is quite striking when seen from the air; the whole bay studded with islands might be shining clear, with a bank of clouds over the mainland, stopping sharply at the shore. Or the land could be sunny and the bay clouded over.

Sometimes, on still warm days, we have a temperature inversion: warm air above traps cooler air below and holds in the pollution from tourist traffic exhaust on Route One. The air is bad to breathe on these days.

In Camden the difference in temperature and humidity between the coast and inland is striking. As one walks downhill toward the harbor, the temperature can drop noticeably and the air fills with humidity. In general the inland temperatures are more extreme than on the coast. In the winter, Hope might be -10°F., Camden and Rockport 0°F and the islands might be.

+10° F. In the summer, we could have the reverse: Hope 85°, C-R, 75° and the islands 65°.

Our storms are generally formed by warm moist air moving up from the south and encountering the edge of a cold high pressure air mass. A counter-clock wise swirl of winds forms along this edge and the resulting storm moves in from the south west and often hits us with the northeasterly winds that spin off its northern, leading edge. It blows hard, slams us with rain and is called a "Nor'easter".

To fishermen, a wind that changes from N.E. to N.W. "backens" in the counter-clock-wise motion that means a low pressure zone and storm. When it "veers" in the other direction (clockwise), it means that fine weather is moving in.

Storms hit Camden hardest from the Southeast and east, while Rockport is completely open to the south and most vulnerable to wind and waves from that direction. Storm damage is also affected by high tides, which average 9.6 feet in the midcoast area

We are strongly affected by the climate and varying weather. The weather is not a frivolous topic of conversation. It governs our lives and those of the plants and other animals around us. Unusual weather will cause some plants to flourish and hold others back. Some animal populations will explode and others seem to disappear. Our energy use, our work, productivity, play and travel are all influenced by the weather. We learn to respond to what the day and the season bring us on the variable coast: we cut wood in the cold, boat in good weather, do indoor work and rest in the storms, and stay out of the fields and woods during mud season.

GEOLOGY

Underneath our houses and streets, under the forests and ponds, under Penobscot Bay beside us, are layers of ancient rocks, laid down beneath old seas. Most of this old rock is covered over by the debris of the more recent glaciers and sediments from the most recent advance of the sea. But the old bedrock shows itself in places. You see it when you walk along the rocky shore, when you climb Mt. Battie or Bald Mountain, on the Millerite Ledges over Megunticook Lake, in the roadcut on the Turnpike (Rt. 52) and on any ledges or outcroppings.

Most of our upper bedrock was deposited as sediments of clay, silt, sand and marine life along the edge of the ancient continent in Cambrian and Ordovician times, between 600 and 400 million years ago (m.y.a.) These sediments, over time and under the weight of overlying layers, turned into sedimentary rocks: shales, sandstones, limestones.

The events that followed can be explained by "continental drift". According to this theory, our continents were made from the splitting and sliding of an ancient continent (Pangaea), which broke up and reassembled several times in the past 700 million years. It appears, from the geologic record left in the bedrock of Maine, that the old continental plate 'Gondwanaland', with what is now Africa on its leading edge, began pushing towards "North America" about 440 m.y.a, and continued for about 50 million years until the edge of "Africa" collided with where we are now, in Maine.

On the leading edge of "Africa", volcanos produced igneous rocks (ryolite,

Particle size & nature of sediments	clay < .004 mm.	silt < .06 mm.	sand < 2 mm.	skeletons of tiny plants & animals .1 - 4 mm.
↓ Sedimentary Rocks	↓ shales	↓	↓ sandstone	↓ limestone
↓ Metamorphic Rocks	↓ slates ↓ schists		↓ quartzite	↓ marble

increasing pressure

erosion & sediments

erosion

Ancient sea

Ancient Continent

sediments

HOW THE CONTINENTS MAY HAVE DRIFTED

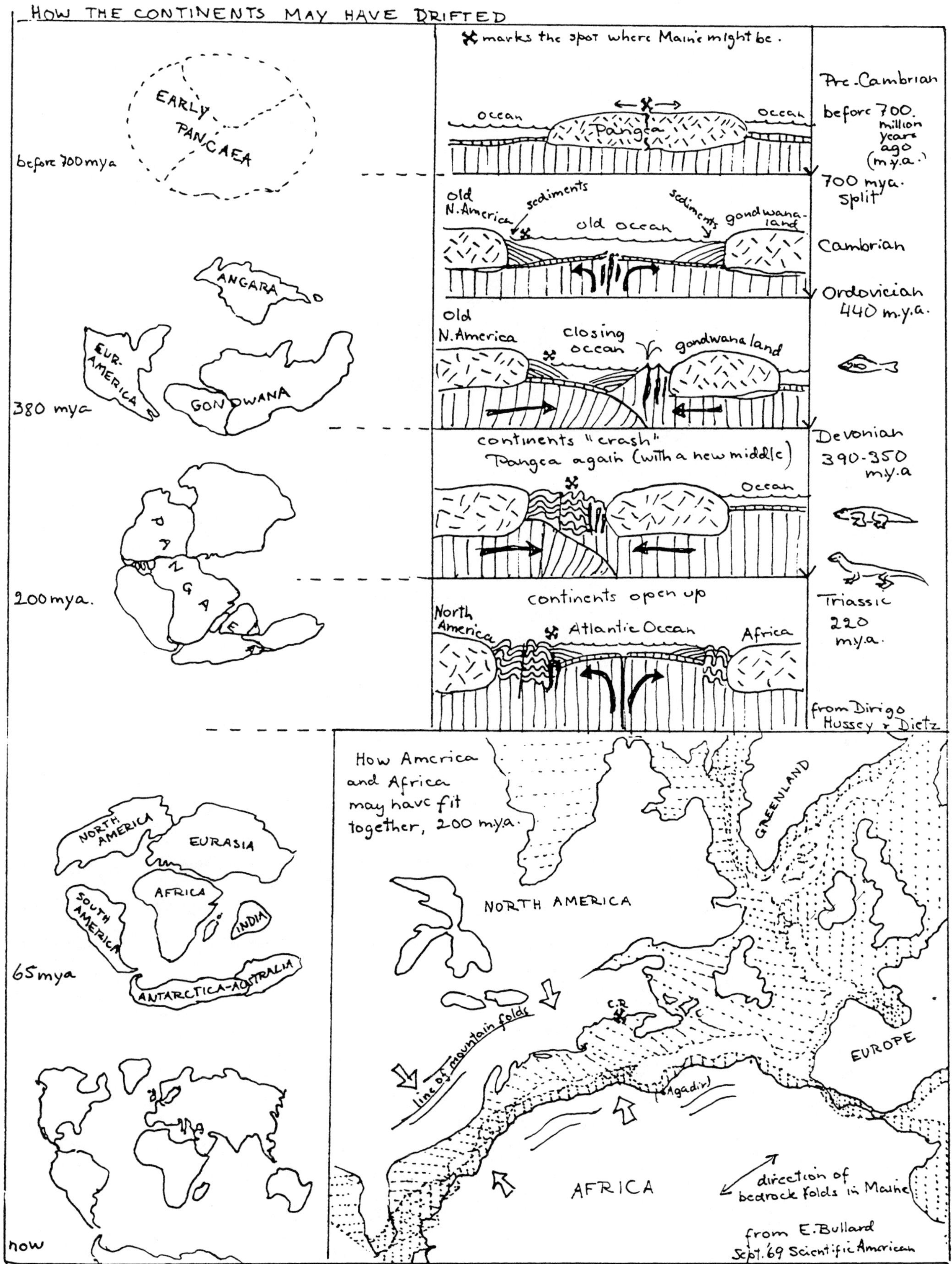

GEOLOGY

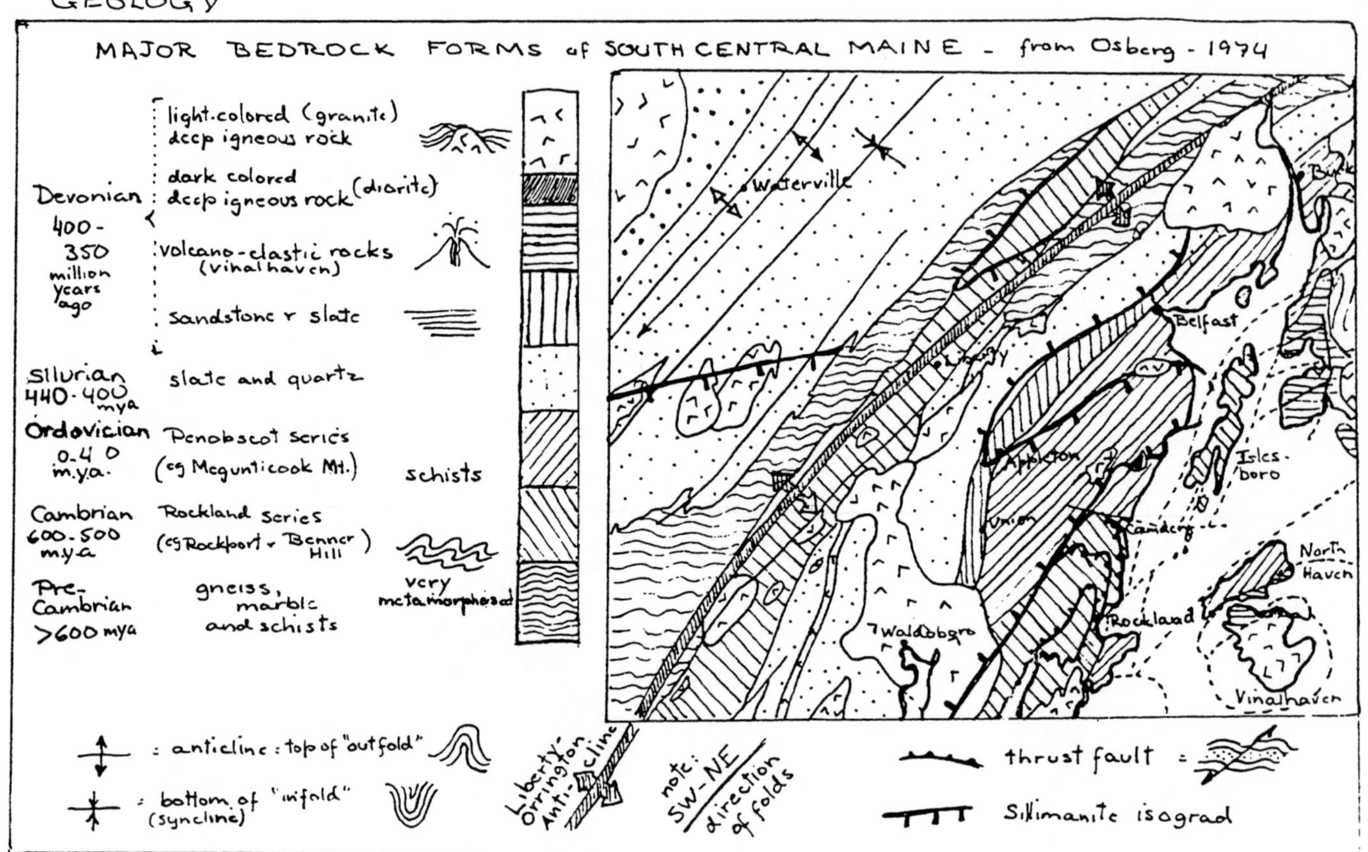

tuff, andesite) that are now found on some of the islands of Penobscot Bay (Vinalhaven and North Haven, ..). As the continents squeezed closer together, the earlier sedimentary rocks buckled into great mountain folds along a north-east south west (SW ↗ NE) direction. They were pressed and heated and became "metamorphosed": changed into schists, quartzite and marble, which is what we have now underneath us. The fossils in the limestone were compressed beyond recognition except for some metamorphosed fossils, from the Ordovician, to be found over on Benner Hill. Mount Battie is quartzite, Mt. Megunticook is schist. We have quarried bands of "marble" under Rockport, Rockland, Lincolnville, Thomaston and Union, to extract the lime used in making cement and plaster.

The great pressure also caused beds of rock to break and slide along each other, up and down, U/D = , or one layer over another, = . There is such a fault going right through Camden, up Mechanic St. and between Ragged and Bald Mountains.

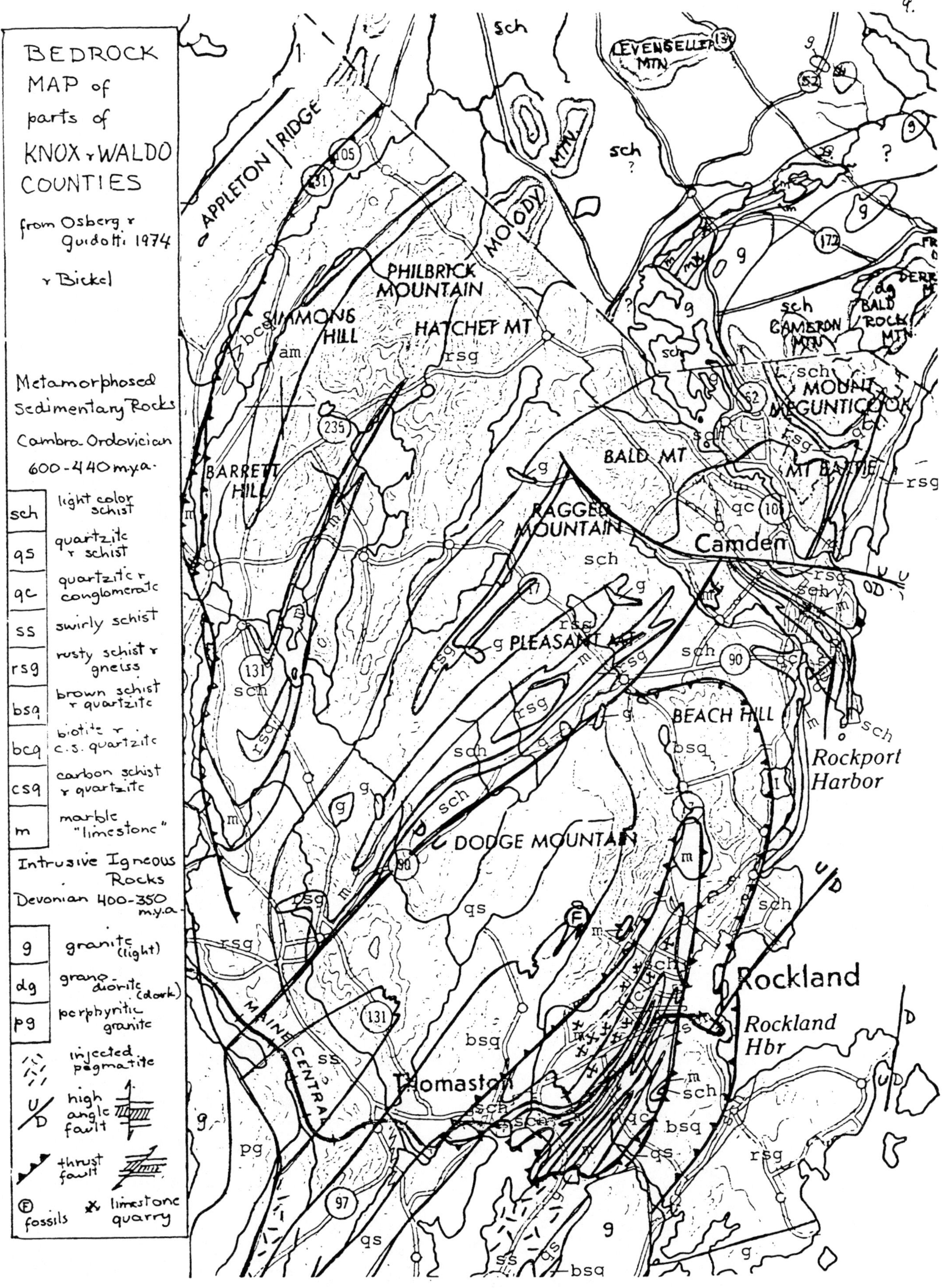
BEDROCK MAP of parts of KNOX & WALDO COUNTIES
from Osberg & Guidotti 1974 & Bickel
Metamorphosed Sedimentary Rocks
Cambro-Ordovician 600-440 m.y.a.
sch light color schist
qs quartzite & schist
qc quartzite & conglomerate
ss swirly schist
rsg rusty schist & gneiss
bsq brown schist & quartzite
bcq biotite & c.s. quartzite
csq carbon schist & quartzite
m marble "limestone"
Intrusive Igneous Rocks
Devonian 400-350 m.y.a.
g granite (light)
dg granodiorite (dark)
pg porphyritic granite
injected pegmatite
U/D high angle fault
thrust fault
F fossils
limestone quarry
LEVENSELLER MTN
APPLETON RIDGE
MOODY MTN.
PHILBRICK MOUNTAIN
SIMMONS HILL
HATCHET MT
CAMERON MTN
BALD ROCK MTN
MOUNT MEGUNTICOOK
BALD MT
MT BATTIE
BARRETT HILL
RAGGED MOUNTAIN
Camden
PLEASANT MT
BEACH HILL
Rockport Harbor
DODGE MOUNTAIN
Rockland
Rockland Hbr
MAINE CENTRAL
Thomaston

10.

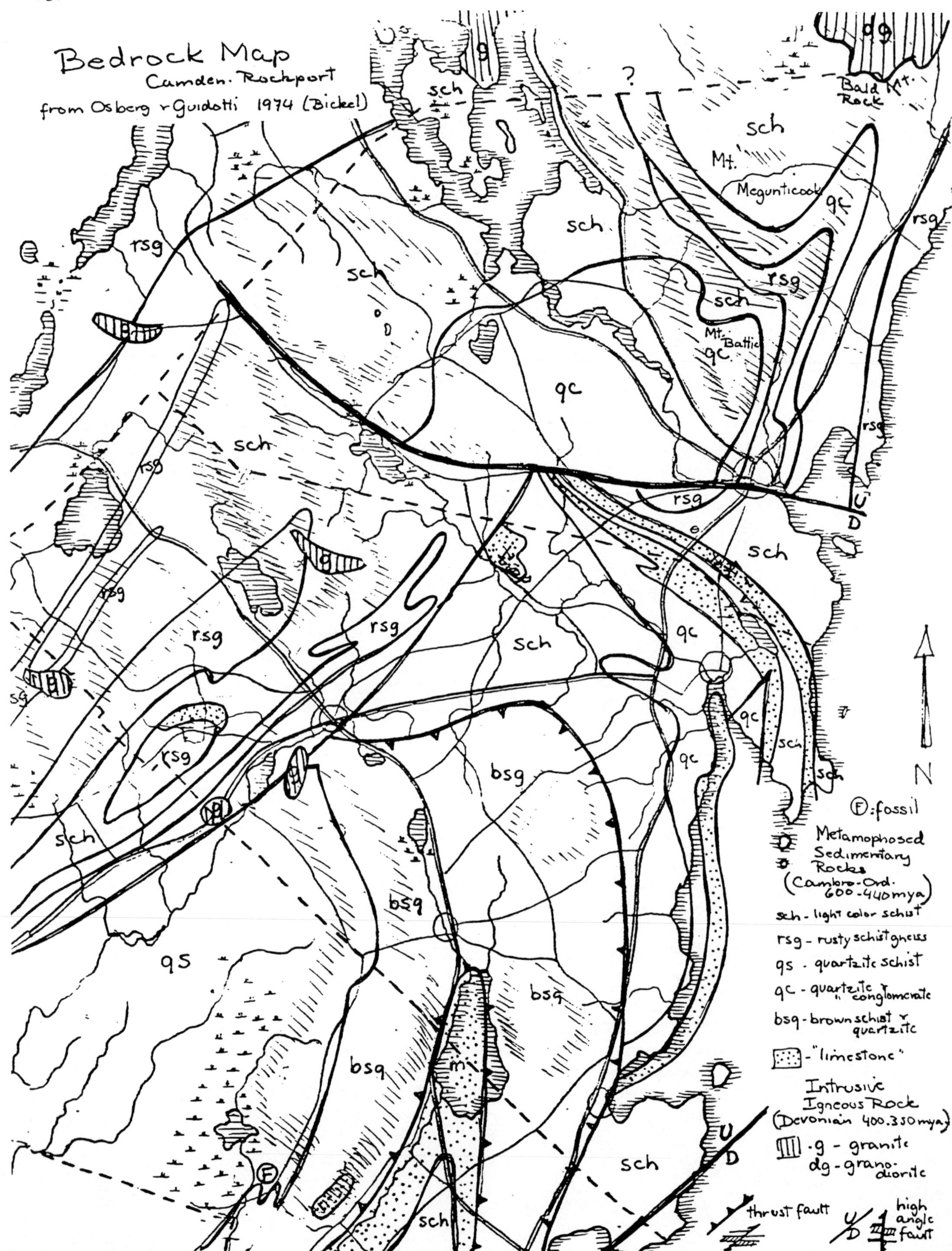

Bedrock Map
Camden-Rockport
from Osberg & Guidotti 1974 (Bickel)
sch
g
dg
?
Bald Mt.
Rock
sch
Mt.
Megunticook
qc
rsg
sch
rsg
sch
rsg
sch
Mt. Battie
qc
qc
sch
rsg
rsg
U
D
sch
rsg
g
rsg
qc
rsg
sch
qc
rsg
sch
qc
sch
sch
bsg
sch
bsq
qs
bsg
bsq
m
sch
sch
U
D
N
F :fossil
Metamophosed
Sedimentary
Rocks
(Cambro-Ord. 600-440mya)
sch - light color schist
rsg - rusty schist gneiss
qs - quartzite schist
qc - quartzite & conglomerate
bsq - brown schist & quartzite
- "limestone"
Intrusive
Igneous Rock
(Devonian 400-350mya)
g - granite
dg - grano-diorite
thrust fault
high angle fault
U
D

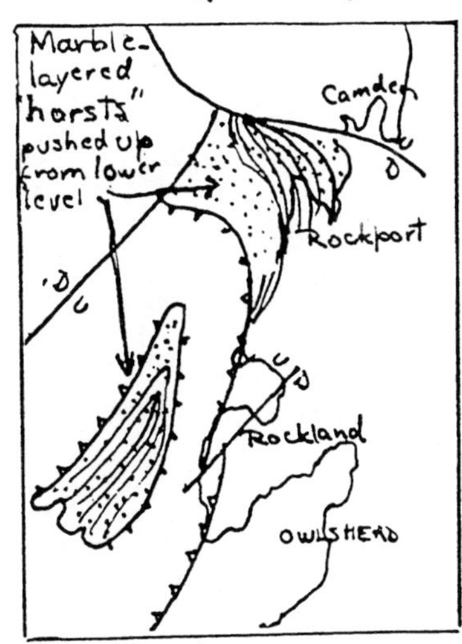

In some places, blocks of lower rock were pushed up to a higher level: the "marble" layers in Rockport and Rockland were such "horsts" pushed up from below. The south east sides of Appleton Ridge and Dodge Mountain are along thrust faults. Route 90 seems to run along another fault. The south west shear faces of Megunticook, Bald and Ragged Mtns. may have been caused by faulting as well as by scraping glaciers.

Under the great folds, stronger changes were taking place. Some rocks were changed into granite and darker diorite: heated, melted, and, very slowly, recrystalized. Hot, melted rock (magma) was injected into cracks in the older rock, cooling to form darker or lighter veins (dikes).

All this happened at the same time the Appalachian Mountains were being formed, by the same forces, before 300 million years ago, before much life had made its way out of the water. Since then, the "collided" continents drifted apart again (200 m.y.a. in the Triassic) leaving the Atlantic Ocean between Maine and its possible twin on the edge of Africa. (The rocks on this part of the Maine coast appear to match those on the north west coast of Africa)

Devonian 350 m.y.a. — 300 m.y.a Mississippian - Penn. — 250 m.y.a Permian — 200 mya Triassic — 150 m.y.a Jurassic — 100 mya Cretaceous

Amphibians, reptiles and, finally, mammals slowly colonized the land, following the plant life that emerged first. But there is no record in the rock of all that. Several miles of over-lying rock were eroded away by water & then scraped by great glaciers, 1 million years ago in the Pleistocene. It is as though nothing had happened for 300 million years.

There had been glacial advances before, but most of the evidence we find here is from the last of the four Pleistocene glaciers: the Wisconsin advance which started only 55 thousand years ago. Think how recent that is, com-

GEOLOGY

pared to the age of the bedrock beneath, 450 million years old.

As the ice built up, about a mile thick, it pressed the land down under its great weight. It scraped and scoured the old mountain folds, pushing slowly to the south east, out of a focus in Labrador,

leaving its tracks diagonally across the lines of the old folds and faults.

Where the ice found valleys in the same direction, it sheared off the walls into steep cliffs, like the Millerite Ledges and the south west sides of Bald and Ragged Mountains. The steep face of Mt. Battie probably had its bare face "plucked" by the over-riding glacier. Many other land features show the direction of the glacier. There are scratches (striations) on ledges where stones were dragged along by the glacier over bedrock (Clam Cove, Mt. Battie.). There are crescent chips knocked out of bedrock by rocks embedded in the glacier (rock island in Megunticook Lake near Bog Bridge). Great long (½ mile) mounds of mixed till, called drumlins, that point in the direction of the glacier were dumped as the glacier went over small obstructions. When you look at a topographic map of Lincolnville, you can see that many of the cleared fields lie N.W. - S.E. because of the way the glacier left the land (the fields are on better drained high lands) Some ponds have been gouged out in this direction; others lie N.E. - S.W. in the direction of the valleys between the old mountain folds.

As the glacier retreated, about 12,000 years ago, it left a broad layer of mixed "till" (sand, gravel and boulders), a "ground moraine" [gm] on the land. The retreating edge of the melting ice dropped series of "washboard moraines", ridges of sediment left by each short period of melting. Lincolnville is covered with them and

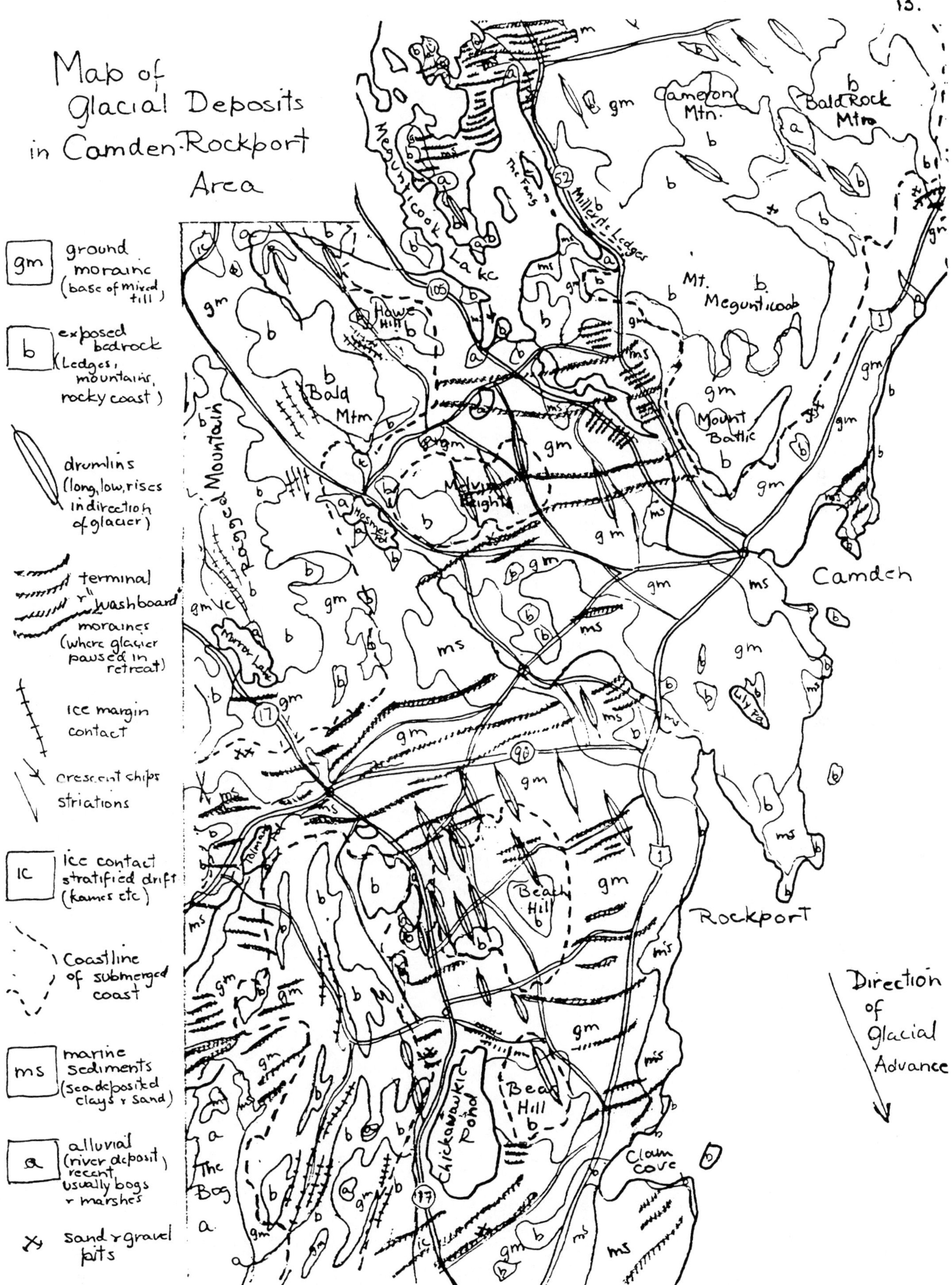

Map of Glacial Deposits in Camden-Rockport Area
gm
ground moraine (base of mixed till)
b
exposed bedrock (Ledges, mountains, rocky coast)
drumlins (long, low, rises in direction of glacier)
terminal r "washboard" moraines (where glacier paused in retreat)
ice margin contact
crescent chips
striations
ic
ice contact stratified drift (kames etc)
Coastline of submerged coast
ms
marine sediments (sea deposited clays r sand)
a
alluvial (river deposit, recent usually bogs r marshes)
sand r gravel pits
Cameron Mtn.
Bald Rock Mtn
Megunticook Lake
Millerite Ledges
Mt. Megunticook
Howe Hill
Bald Mtn
Ragged Mountain
Mount Battie
Melvin Heights
Hosmer Pd
Camden
Mirror Lake
Lily Pd
Tolman Pd
Beech Hill
Rockport
Chickawaukie Pond
Bear Hill
Clam Cove
The Bog
Direction of Glacial Advance

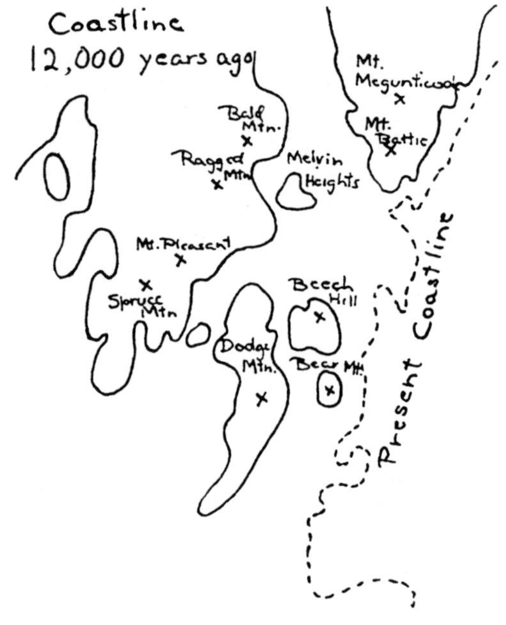

there are some series along Megunticook River, under Upper Washington and Upper Mountain Streets. Some moraine deposits blocked the drainage of old rivers, causing marshes, bogs and strange contorted drainage patterns. We dig into the till under us at places where it is sorted (usually moraines) to get gravel for building and road making (gravel pits: under Mt. Battie, on Spruce Mtn., near Oak Hill Cemetary, etc.). The glacier also left large rocks (erratics) in strange places, like Balance Rock on Lake Megunticook. It is possible that "the Fang" in Lake Megunticook, with its little train of islands, is a boulder train left where two arms of the glacier met. The rushing melt waters of the glacier left the beautiful round polished stones that we find on some of our beaches.

The rising sea followed the melting glacier back over the buckled land. Under its waters, impermeable clays and fine silts were laid down (marine sediments ms). The sea made islands of Beech Hill, Bear Hill, Dodge Mtn. and Melvin Heights. Mt. Megunticook and Ragged Mt., Spruce Mtn. & Mount Pleasant were on long peninsulas that reached into the sea.

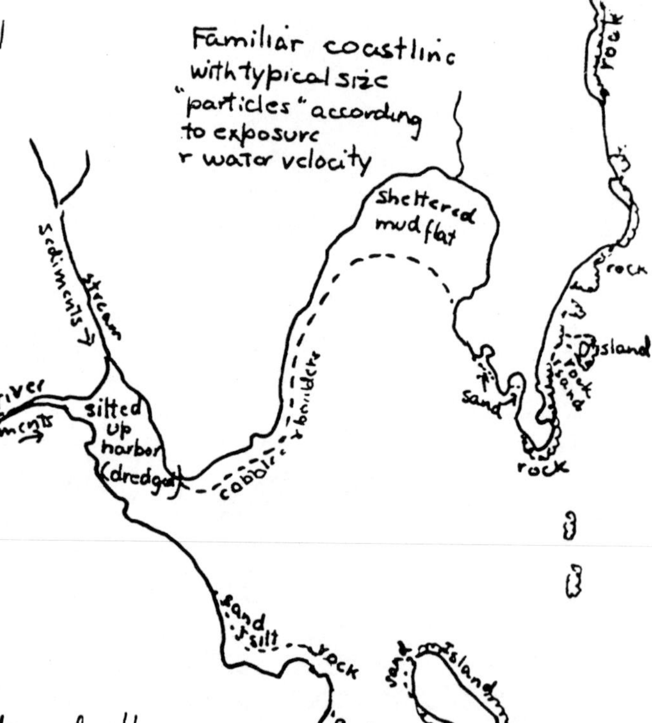

About 10,000 years ago, the land gradually rebounded and the sea retreated to where it is now. The sea works constantly on our coasts, cutting at the exposed rock, rolling the boulders, sorting the sand

and mud in the sheltered places.

Our cover of soil and forest is very recent. We don't have rich layers of topsoil like the Central Plains. Our soils were formed on the base of glacial till and bedrock. These soils are typically brown or grey brown, of the spodsol family, formed by the erosion of acid rocks and debris where there is a fair amount of rain (40" a year). Decomposed leaves and needles of the forest trees, and now, acid rain from the industrial Midwest, further contribute to the acidity of the soil. Percolating rain water leaches many of the minerals and nutrients out of the surface layers, so the soils may not be very fertile.

The type of soil depends on the slope of the land, the temperature and rain fall, the nature and permeability of the parent material, in our case mostly schisty glacial till and some marine clay. Much of our soil is sandy loam, which may dry out too quickly if it is shallow, sloped and close to the bedrock. Or the soil may not drain well for part of the year if it is less sloped, in a depresscion, and underlain by compact impermeable glacial till or marine clays. Unsorted glacial till is almost as impermeable as clay, because the smaller particles of sand and silt pack tightly into all the spaces between the rocks and gravel. So, much of our land is water-logged

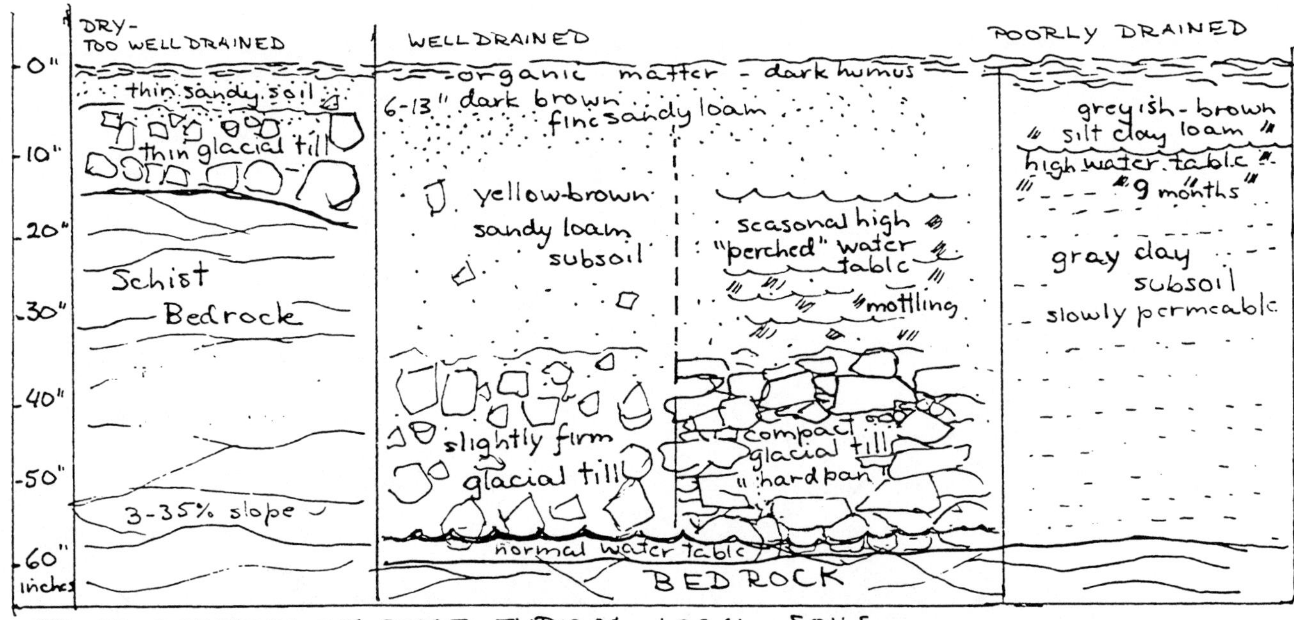

CROSS SECTIONS OF SOME TYPICAL LOCAL SOILS

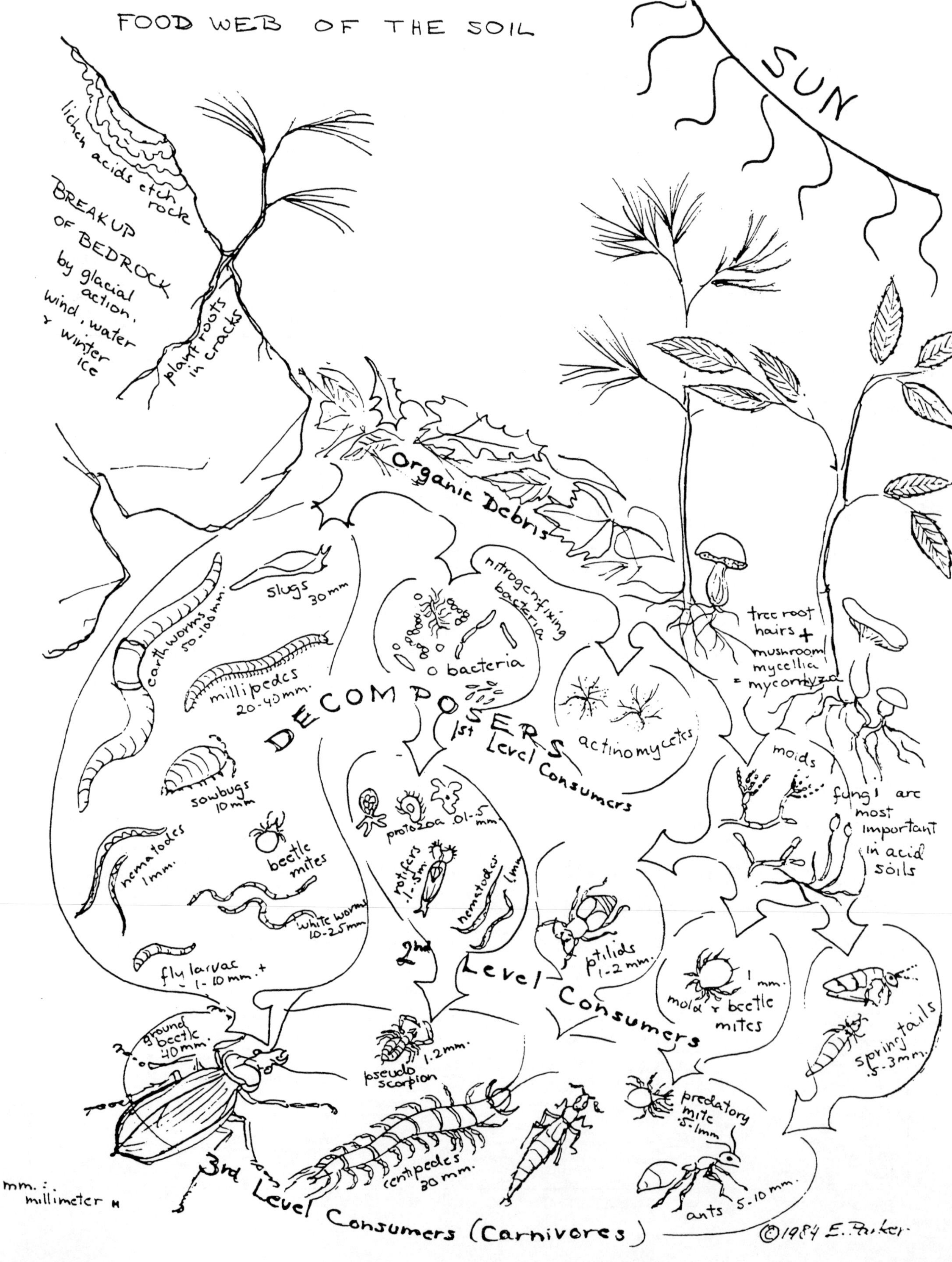
FOOD WEB OF THE SOIL
SUN
lichen acids etch rock
BREAKUP OF BEDROCK by glacial action, wind, water & winter ice
plant roots in cracks
Organic Debris
slugs 30 mm
earthworms 50-100 mm.
millipedes 20-40 mm.
nitrogen fixing bacteria
o bacteria
DECOMPOSERS
1st Level Consumers
actinomycetes
tree root hairs + mushroom mycelia = mycorrhyza
molds
fungi are most important in acid soils
sowbugs 10 mm
nematodes 1mm.
beetle mites
protozoa .01-.5 mm
rotifers .1-.5 m.
nematodes 1 mm
white worms 10-25 mm
fly larvae 1-10 mm.+
2nd Level Consumers
ptilids 1-2 mm.
1 mm. mold & beetle mites
springtails .5-3 mm.
ground beetle 40 mm.
pseudo scorpion 1.2 mm.
predatory mite .5-1 mm
centipedes 30 mm.
ants 5-10 mm.
3rd Level Consumers (Carnivores)
mm. = millimeter
©1984 E. Parker

from late fall to spring and shows grey mottling and rust spots in the profile. Another phenomenon is "mud season", usually in March, when the top layer of soil defrosts first but cannot drain away because of the frost in the ground below. The soil structure is very easily damaged at this time and should not be compressed. We also have some muck and peat soils that are never really drained, so the plant material is not broken down because of the low oxygen content.

In the dark humus layer on the surface of the soil, many organisms are working to break down the organic material that falls to the forest floor: leaves, wood, bodies of animals. These organisms, bacteria, fungi, worms, crustacea, insects and some small mammals, change the decaying plant material into nutrients to be used by the living plants, while building a thicker layer of topsoil.

Our soils can be made fertile by increasing the humus content. We must care for and build up what we have. We must keep it covered with protective vegetation so that it doesn't erode. We must also protect our water supplies. Unwise tree cutting and the construction of roads and houses can disrupt the watersheds that collect our groundwater and fill our lakes. We must take care that pollutants do not drain into the ground water in the glacial and bedrock aquifers below so that we do not poison our water supply.

GEOLOGY
Megunticook Lake
CAMDEN
Hosmer Pond
Camden Harbor
Curtis I.
ROCKPORT
Deadman Pt.
LAND
Chickawaukie Pond
Soils
from Maine Coastal Inventory 1977

Key to Soils

ALLUVIAL SOILS *

3 Rumney — Saco
4 Saco — Organic soils

GLACIAL TILLS

10 Hollis — Charlton soils, 3-15% slopes
12 Hollis — Charlton soils, rocky phase, 0-15% slopes
13 Hollis — Charlton soils, rocky phase, 15-45% slopes
14 Hollis — Paxton soils, 0-15% slopes
15 Hollis — Paxton soils, 15-25% slopes
16 Hollis — Paxton soils, rocky phase, 0-15% slopes
17 Hollis — Paxton soils, rocky phase, 15-45% slopes
18 Hollis — Buxton — Scantic soils, 0-15% slopes
19 Hollis — Buxton — Scantic soils, 15-30% slopes
20 Hollis, rocky phase — Rockland, 0-45% slopes
26 Charlton — Sutton, stony phase, 0-8% slopes
27 Charlton — Sutton, stony phase, 8-15% slopes
28 Charlton — Hollis, 15-25% slopes
29 Charlton — Hollis, stony phase, 15-25% slopes
32 Sutton - Leicester, 0-8% slopes
34 Sutton — Ridgebury, 0-8% slopes
35 Sutton — Ridgebury, stony phase, 0-8% slopes
40 Paxton — Woodbridge, 3-8% slopes
41 Paxton — Woodbridge, 8-15% slopes
42 Paxton — Woodbridge, stony phase, 3-15% slopes
43 Paxton — Hollis, 8-15% slopes
44 Paxton — Hollis, 15-25% slopes
45 Paxton — Hollis, stony phase, 15-30% slopes
50 Woodbridge — Paxton, 8-15% slopes
51 Woodbridge — Paxton, stony phase, 8-15% slopes
52 Woodbridge — Ridgebury, 0-8% slopes
53 Woodbridge — Ridgebury, stony phase, 0-8% slopes
55 Ridgebury — Woodbridge, 0-8% slopes
56 Ridgebury — Woodbridge, stony phase, 0-8% slopes

WATER DEPOSITED SOILS

(over clays)

122 Buxton — Belgrade, 0-15% slopes
123 Buxton — Scantic, 0-8% slopes
128 Scantic — Buxton, 0-8% slopes
129 Scantic — Biddeford, 0-3% slopes
137 Belgrade — Scantic, 0-8% slopes
143 Swanton — Scantic, 0-3% slopes

GLACIAL OUTWASH SOILS

(over sand & gravel)

152 Hinckley — Sudbury, 0-15% slopes
153 Hinckley — Windsor, 15-30% slopes
154 Sudbury — Walpole, 0-3% slopes
156 Windsor - Deerfield, 0-8% slopes
158 Ninigret - Walpole, 0-8% slopes
159 Walpole — Scarboro, 0-3% slopes

FINENESS of PARTICLES
- .5 - 2mm. sand
- .5-.002mm. silt
- .002mm. clay

mixture = loam

h: hardpan
d: droughty
w: stays wet

9M - Organic soils (usually a bog or marsh)

new "frigid" soil names in (-)	Slope	drainage	depth to bedrock (inches)	(Surface) Texture	Permeability
	mostly RIVER Deposits				
Rumney	0-3	poor (floods)	>60"	fine sandy loam	rapid
Saco	0-3	very poor (floods)	>60"	silt loam	mod.
Organic	0-3	Very poor (floods)	>60"	organics in loamy sand	rapid
	mostly GLACIAL TILL				
Hollis (Lyman)	3-35	too much d.	<20	fine sandy loam (ledge)	mod-rapid
Charlton	3-35	good	>60	fine sandy loam (stoney)	mod-rapid
Paxton (Marlow)	3-25	good	>60	fine sandy loam (hardpan)	mod.-slow
Rockland	8-35	too much	<20	loamy sand to silt loam	mod. rapid
Sutton (Peru)	0-15	mod. well	>60	fine sandy loam	slow
Leicester	0-18	mod. poor	>60	fine sandy loam	mod-slow
Ridgebury (Brayton)	0-8	poor	>60	Sandy loam (stoney) h.	slow
Woodbridge (Peru)	3-35	mod. well	>60	fine sandy loam stoney h.	Slow
	mostly SEA or LAKE deposited.				
Buxton	0-25	mod. to poor w	>60	silty loam clay below	very slow
Scantic	0-8	poor w	>60	silty loam (clay below)	slow
Biddeford	0-3	very poor	>60	silty clay loam (Clay below)	very slow
Belgrade	0-15	mod. well	>60	very fine sandy loam	mod. slow
Swanton (Swanville)	0-3	mod. poor	>60	fine sandy loam (silty clay below)	slow
	mostly GLACIAL OUTWASH				
Hinkley (Masardis)	3-35	too much	>60	Sandy loam (sand below)	very rapid
Sudbury (Machias)	0-3	mod. well	>60	Sandy loam (sand below)	very rapid
Walpole	0-3	poor	>60	fine sandy loam (sand below)	rapid
Windsor (Adams)	3-25	too much d	>60	Loamy sand (sand below)	very rapid
Deerfield	0-8	mod-well	>60	Loamy sand (sand below)	very rapid
Ninigret (Madawaska)	3-8	mod-well	>60	fine loamy sand	rapid
Scarboro (Searsport)	0-3	very poor	>60	Loamy fine sand	very rapid

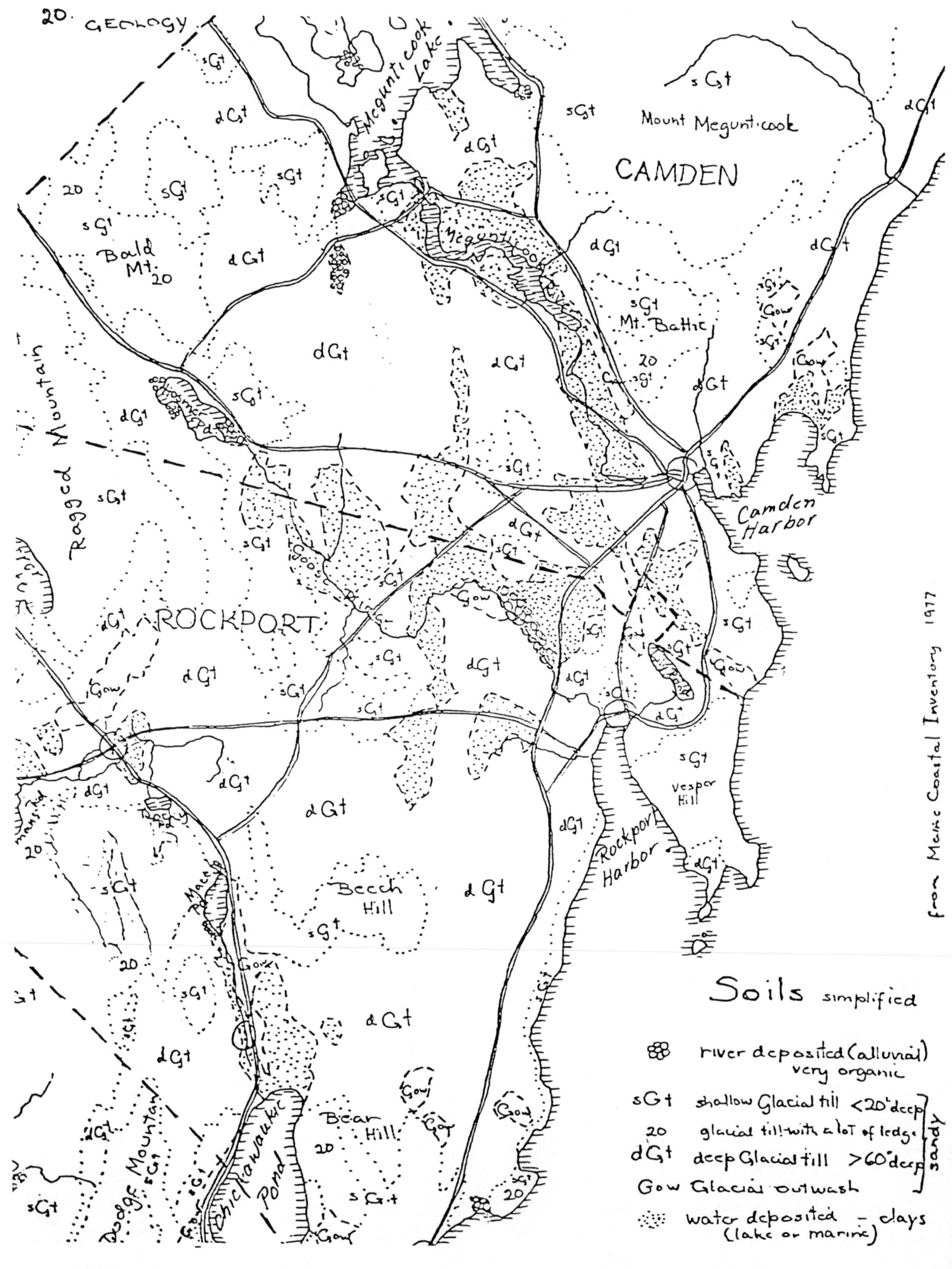
Meguntıcook Lake
Mount Meguntıcook
CAMDEN
Bald Mt. 20
Megunticook
Mt. Battie
Ragged Mountain
ROCKPORT
Camden Harbor
Vesper Hill
Rockport Harbor
Beech Hill
Bear Hill
Chickawaukie Pond
Dodge Mountain
Soils simplified
river deposited (alluvial) very organic
sGt shallow Glacial till <20" deep
20 glacial till with a lot of ledge
dGt deep Glacial till >60" deep
sandy
Gow Glacial outwash
water deposited - clays (lake or marine)
from Maine Coastal Inventory 1977

ROCKY SHORE

We live on the edge of the rocky shore of the Penobscot Bay. The last heavy glaceer scraped it bare and pressed it down until the melting sea reached into the old river valleys and turned the outer hills into islands.

You can go down to the sea and walk along the rocks. Most of the shore line is privately owned but there are some landing places and public parks.(1) There are more different kinds of animals to be seen here than in any other place nearby (except perhaps in a drop of pond water or in garden soil) You must go down at low tide. Lift the mats of sea weed to see what is hiding under them. Look into pools of water left above the tide. You will see animals belonging to most of the groups on the "evolutionary tree", from simple sponges to vertebrates (which include you). The variety of body forms is greater than anything imagined in science fiction.

The creatures of the rocky shore must be able to survive out of water part of the time, or else to follow the tide down. They must resist the drying action of the sun and wind. They must also be able to hang onto the rocks and withstand the force of the waves, or else hide between the rocks and under the sea weed. Every day the tide comes in and out twice, as this part of the earth swings under the pulling line of the moon. The average height of the tide in our area is 9.6 feet. Twice a month the earth, the moon and the sun are in line, which makes a very high and very low tide, the "spring" tides. The gentler tides in between, not so high and not so low, are called "neap" tides.

Different plants and animals will live on a level of the shore according to how much of the time it is covered by sea water. The shore is thus divided into "zones", highly visible "bands" of plants and animals. The highest

see p. 23 description

(1) in Camden: Sherman's Point, Eaton's Point, Public Landing, (Laite) Town Beach, and the Camden Hills State Park. In Rockport: Public Landing, Red Ledges, Walker Park, Marine Park. Also: Lincolnville Beach, Ducktrap, Owls Head, Lucia Beach.

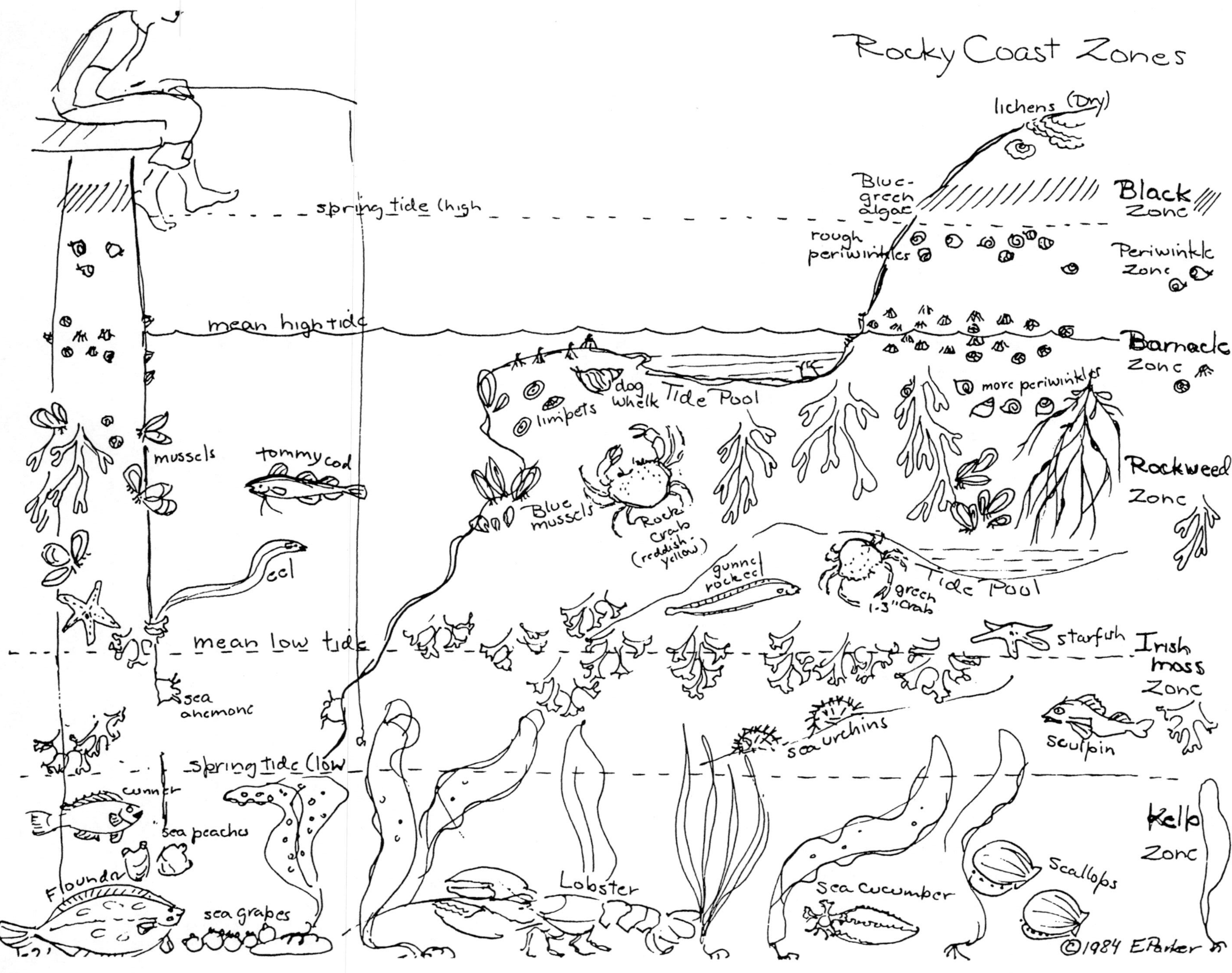
Rocky Coast Zones
lichens (Dry)
Blue-green algae
Black Zone
spring tide (high
rough periwinkles
Periwinkle Zone
mean high tide
Barnacle Zone
more periwinkles
dog whelk
Tide Pool
limpets
mussels
tommy cod
Rockweed Zone
Blue mussels
Rock Crab (reddish-yellow)
eel
gunnel rock eel
green 1-3" Crab
Tide Pool
starfish
Irish moss Zone
mean low tide
sea anemone
sea urchins
sculpin
spring tide (low
cunner
sea peaches
Kelp Zone
Scallops
Flounder
sea grapes
Lobster
Sea Cucumber
©1984 E Parker

band is reached only by the highest spring tide and the lowest band is almost always under water. In between, the shore is covered by water only part of the time, except in the tide pools, little natural aquaria where the water is caught and many interesting things live. These zones are easiest to see where steep rock faces the sea, and on the wood pilings under docks and piers.

The highest level is the A* black zone[1], made by a film of blue-green algae that clings to the rock. It is black when dry but turns dark green and slippery when wet. Above it is bare rock, and then perhaps some orange or grey lichens. Just below the black band, there may be B* a line of rough periwinkles. They can close up tight and stay without moisture for long periods if they need to. Below them is the C* barnacle zone; the rock is white with the cases of barnacles. They also close tight when the tide is out but when it rises, they open their doors and reach out their feathery limbs to rake in tiny organisms floating in the water. Here and there, on bare rock, there might be a limpet, a little volcano-shaped shell clinging tightly to the rock.

Below the barnacles is a thick dark D* band of rockweeds, brown algae, with blue mussels growing between and under them. The mussels are well attached to the rock by fine (byssus) threads. They too close when the tide is down and open when water is up to siphon the food-filled water through their gills. The brown seaweeds here are mostly bladder and spiral wrack, with pimply reproductive tips, and knotted wrack, which looks like black shoe laces with oval air bladders. The rockweeds hold tight to the rocks and are floated up by the air bladders when the tide is in. They lie flat and sprawled in the low tide. Underneath there are crabs lurking, reddish rock crabs and little green crabs. Hiding in wet pockets are shrimpy little amphipods (called "scuds"). There are great

see p. 21 - illustration

numbers of another kind of periwinkle, the common periwinkle, roaming over the rocks and seaweed, scraping the algae coating off with their rasp-like tongues. Closer to the low tide, there are pretty little "smooth" periwinkles, some bright yellow, some striped. The white, rippled, pointy snail shells you find once belonged to dog whelks that prey on the mussels and barnacles by drilling holes in their shells.

Other creatures live attached to the sea weeds: Bryozoa, or "moss" animals, live in tufty, bristly little colonies (eg Bugula) that look like plants themselves. Another bryozoa called "sea lace" (Membranipora) leaves the delicate skeletons of its animals like a coating of lace over the sea weed. Sometimes minute coiled worm tubes (Spirorbis) are attached to the sea weed, looking like flecks of paint. There are also tufty little "red" sea weeds (Polysiphonia) hanging onto the knotted wrack.

Further down again, always wet, usually under water, is the E <u>Irish moss zone</u>, covered by the dark reddish-brown, frilly "red" algae. Irish moss is gathered in some places by people in boats, to be made into carageenan, a food thickener. Carageenan is made in Rockland from irish moss, once gathered along this coast but now imported from far away.

You can only reach the irish moss zone at lowest tide. Under the sea weed there are starfish and some sea urchins. There are even more blue mussels. The starfish feed on mussels and clams by pulling their shells open with their arms & tiny tube feet. There are tiny skeleton "shrimp" that creep like inch worms over the sea weed.

Still further down is the F <u>kelp zone</u>. This is always below water but you can see the flat broad leathery-brown seaweeds washed up on the shore, their holdfasts clutching a stone or big horse mussel. Some kinds of kelps are shaped like palm fronds, with long fingers (oarweed), some have holes, like colanders. They make forests below the low tide level, inhabited by starfish, sea anemones, sea squirts

Northern Starfish. 6"+-

Green Sea Urchin 3"

Irish Moss

Seaweeds (and Companions)

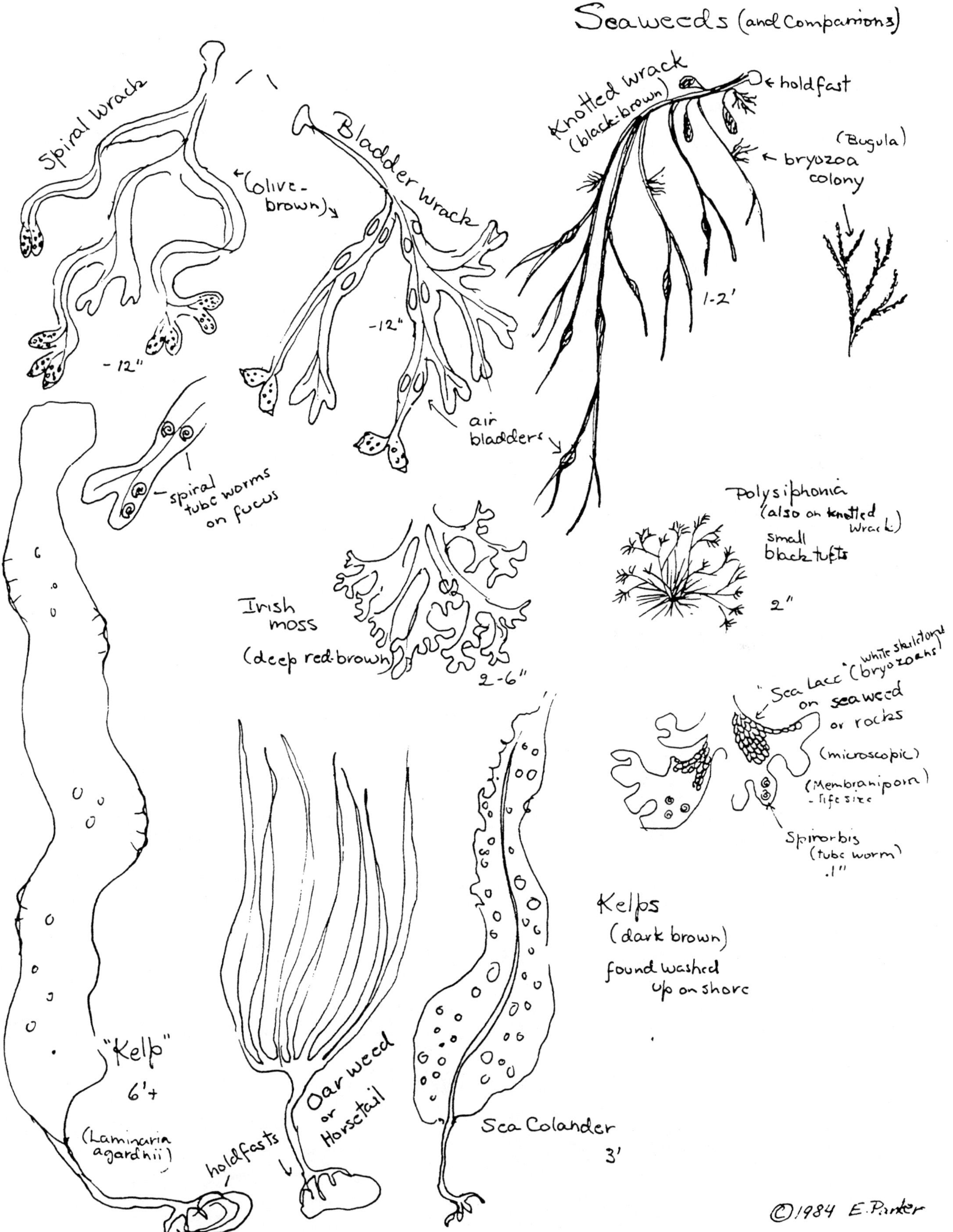

sea cucumbers, swimming worms, tube worms. brittle stars, Rock crabs, sea-slugs, and, of course, the lobster.

There are fish hunting in the kelp forest and off the rocks: cunner, sculpin, gunnel (rock eel), tommycod, eels, searaven and toadfish.

These bands of sea animals and plants vary in width along the shore. You can tell how strong the waves are in each place by what lives there. A steep exposed wall will be white with barnacles, while a sloped beach of small boulders, more sheltered, will have a broad expanse of rockweed, mussels and periwinkles.

Back up the rocky shore, you might find small tide pools that hold still sea water when the tide goes out. The bottom of such a pool may be encrusted with pink calcareous algae and lumpy looking greenish "crumb of bread" sponge. Hiding in the sponge and under stones are flat worms, scale worms, brittle starfish. Sea anemones and bushy hydroids cling to the sides and under overhanging rock, sheltered from waves and sun. Small scud (shrimplike) scoot across and hide in crevices. Here you can see the barnacles open and fishing; perhaps a chiton is moving across the bottom. A hermit crab picks its way along the floor, wearing a large periwinkle shell. A fierce hunting sand worm (Nereis) might be resting under a rock 'til nightfall. Besides rock-weed and irish moss, there could be a piece of bright green sea lettuce (Ulva) and tufts of pink coraline algae, looking like the bryozoan animals. On the surface of the pool, there are sometimes wriggling clusters of "tide pool insects" (Anurida), purplish-grey in color, suspended by surface tension on top of the

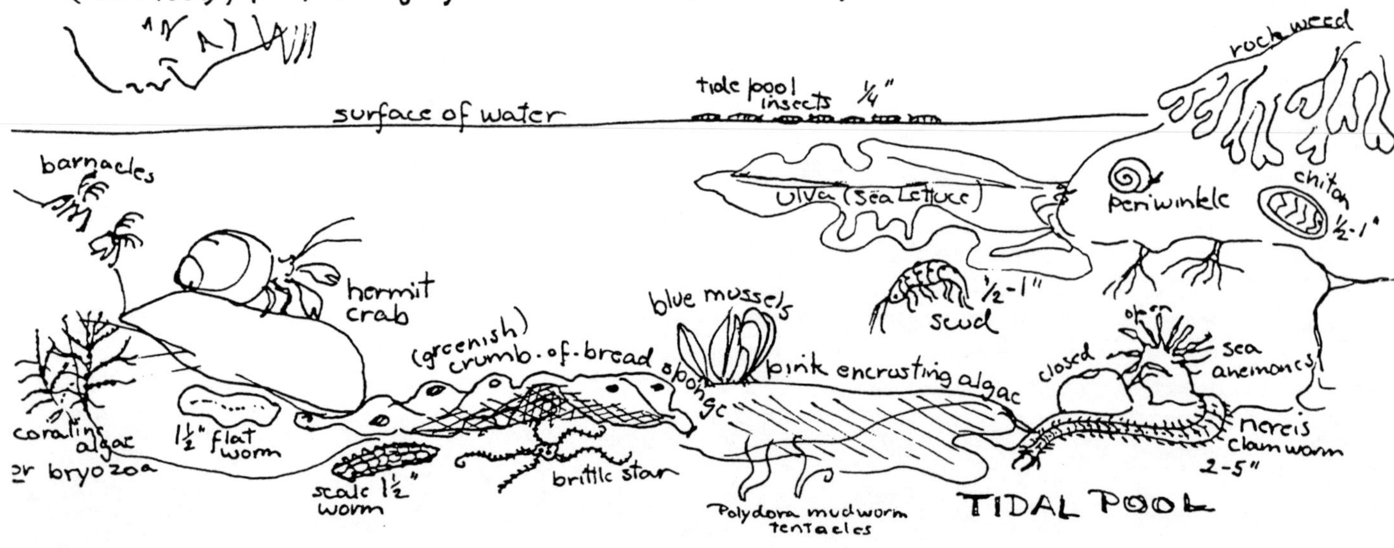

Shore Fish

Pugy (menhaden) grey warm 5-10"

5-10" Herring. (silver-grey)

(Steely blue - black) Mackerel 12"

(silvery) Silversides 3"

Smelt 7-9" (move up rivers in spring) (silver-grey)

Bluefish <30"

Dogfish light grey 2-3'

Cunner 2-18" red brown rocky bottom

Sucker <20'

12" sculpin color like bottom

(green-brown) Tomcod 10"+ 15'+

White Perch grey silver

2'++ Codfish greyish or brownish (mostly further out)

Eel

Flounder 12+" (color varies with bottom)

Skate ("Brownish) 20"

water. These tiny primitive insects also scurry about on the dry rocks, scavenging.

Another place to see rocky shore creatures is on the wood pilings of wharfs as the tide goes out. You can see the same zones on the posts: black (blue-green) algae, white barnacles, blue-black mussels, and, down low where the Irish moss would be: sea anemones, starfish, sea squirts, sea grapes, sea peaches ① In the summer, people go down to fish at the town landings with drop lines. They catch the rocky shore fish, and the fish that come up to river mouths. Some of these fish are good eating though there is debate about how clean harbor fish are. ②

Unlike the mud flats and marshes, the exposed rocky shores are quickly washed clean of sewage and other kinds of water-soluble pollution that is allowed to flow into the sea. But these edges of the land are all vulnerable to oil spills. The oil clings to everything and is absorbed by the tiny organisms low on the food chain. It suffocates the breathing gills of small invertebrates and coats the feathers of sea birds. It works its way up the food chain, interfering with the life cycles of many creatures, poisoning as it goes.

① These last three species are all tunicates, related to vertebrates in that they have a "notochord", a short nerve cord, in their juvenile forms.

② Caught at Camden Town Landing: pogy, herring, smelt, rockfish, seaperch, flounder, sculpin, mackerel, tommy cod, (cod), dog fish, sucker, bluefish, harbor pollock.

③ Also the Great Blackback gull (28-31") - much larger and with black wing backs.

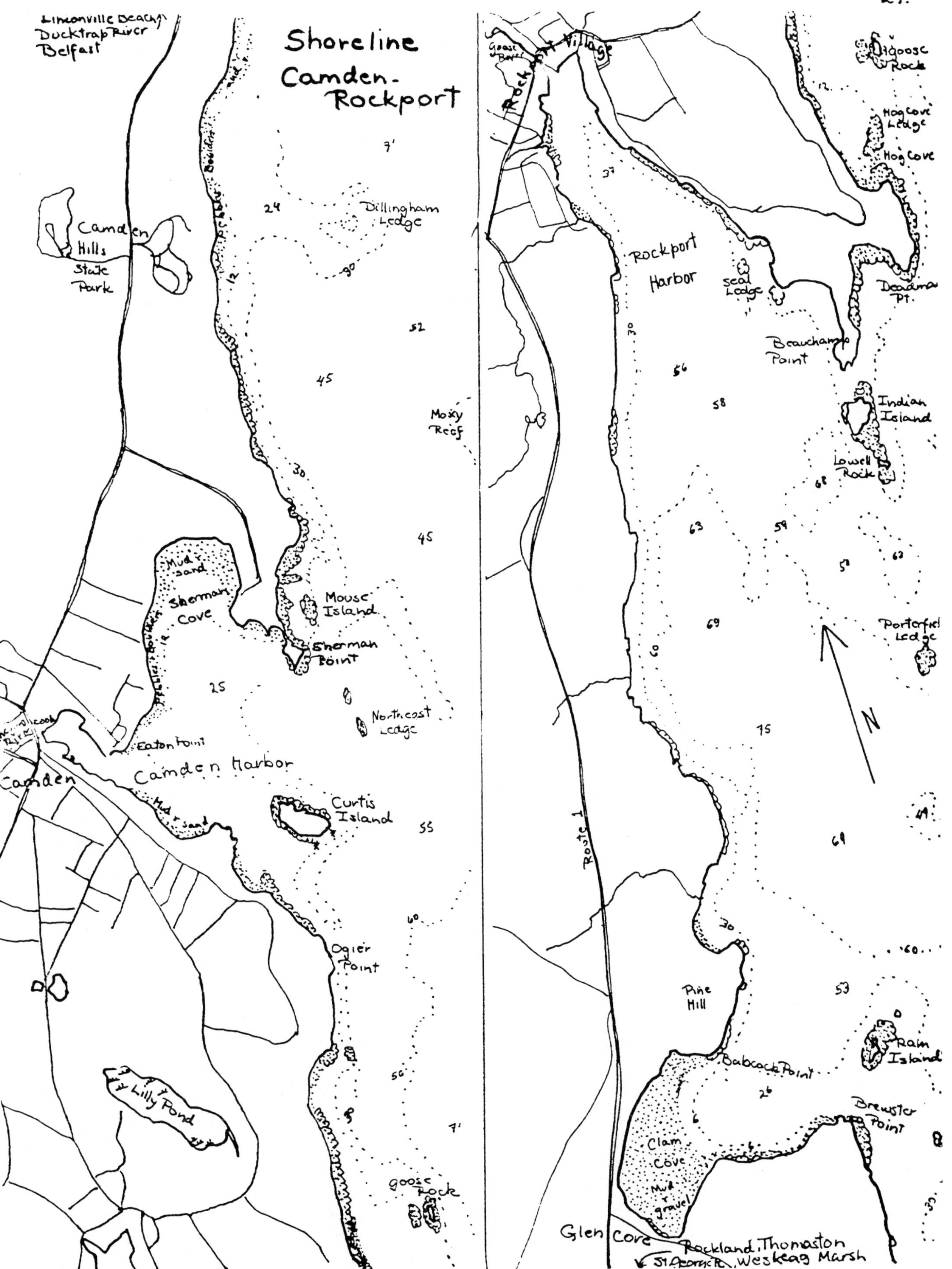
Lincolnville Beach
Ducktrap River
Belfast
Shoreline
Camden-
Rockport
Dillingham Ledge
Camden Hills State Park
Mosky Reef
Mud sand
Sherman Cove
Mouse Island
Sherman Point
Northeast Ledge
Eaton Point
Camden Harbor
Camden
Mud + sand
Curtis Island
Ogier Point
Lilly Pond
goose Rock
Rockport Village
Goose River
Hogoose Rock
Hog Cove Ledge
Hog Cove
Rockport Harbor
Seal Ledge
Deadman Pt.
Beauchamp Point
Indian Island
Lowell Rock
Porterfield Ledge
N
Route 1
Pine Hill
Babcock Point
Ram Island
Brewster Point
Clam Cove
Mud + gravel
Glen Cove
Rockland, Thomaston
St. George R.
Weskeag Marsh

INSHORE · OFFSHORE

Beyond the edge of the lowest tide that can be explored on foot is another world of deeper water, the air above it, the bottoms below and the islands and banks beyond. Who lives where, out there, depends on the kind of bottom, the depth of the water and on the changing temperature and salinity of the water.

Some fish are bottom dwellers ("ground fish") They feed on the crustaceans (shrimps, crabs etc), molluscs (shellfish), sea worms, echinoderms (sea urchins - starfish) that inhabit the bottoms. Many of these fish are members of the flatfish family (blackback or winter flounder, fluke or summer flounder, yellowtail flounder, dab and the great halibut). They like a sticky, muddy sandy bottom that they can hide in or on. Many bottom fish take the color of the ground they lie on. Most of the cod family live near the bottom too. Herds of red hake graze along muddy bottoms, groping along with their feelers. Haddock are more on sand and gravel and cusk hide in boulder bottoms. The cod does a lot of bottom feeding itself. Of other families, the lumpfish clings to rock surfaces with a suction disc, skates flap along like flatfish. The goosefish sits on the bottom, dangling a lure, and opens its great mouth to suck in passersby. The wolffish crushes shellfish with its strong jaws. The lobster lives here too, feeding like the bottom fish, hiding by day in rock crevices or mud burrows and coming out at night to feed.

Some fish live near the surface.

Peridinium
flagellates
ceratium
PHYTOPLANKTON
sea spider larva
fish larva
Foraminifera
globegerina
ZOOPLANKTON
Radiolaria
sea butterfly
copepods
jellyfish medusa
sea urchin larva
crab larva
Diatoms
Noctiluca
worm

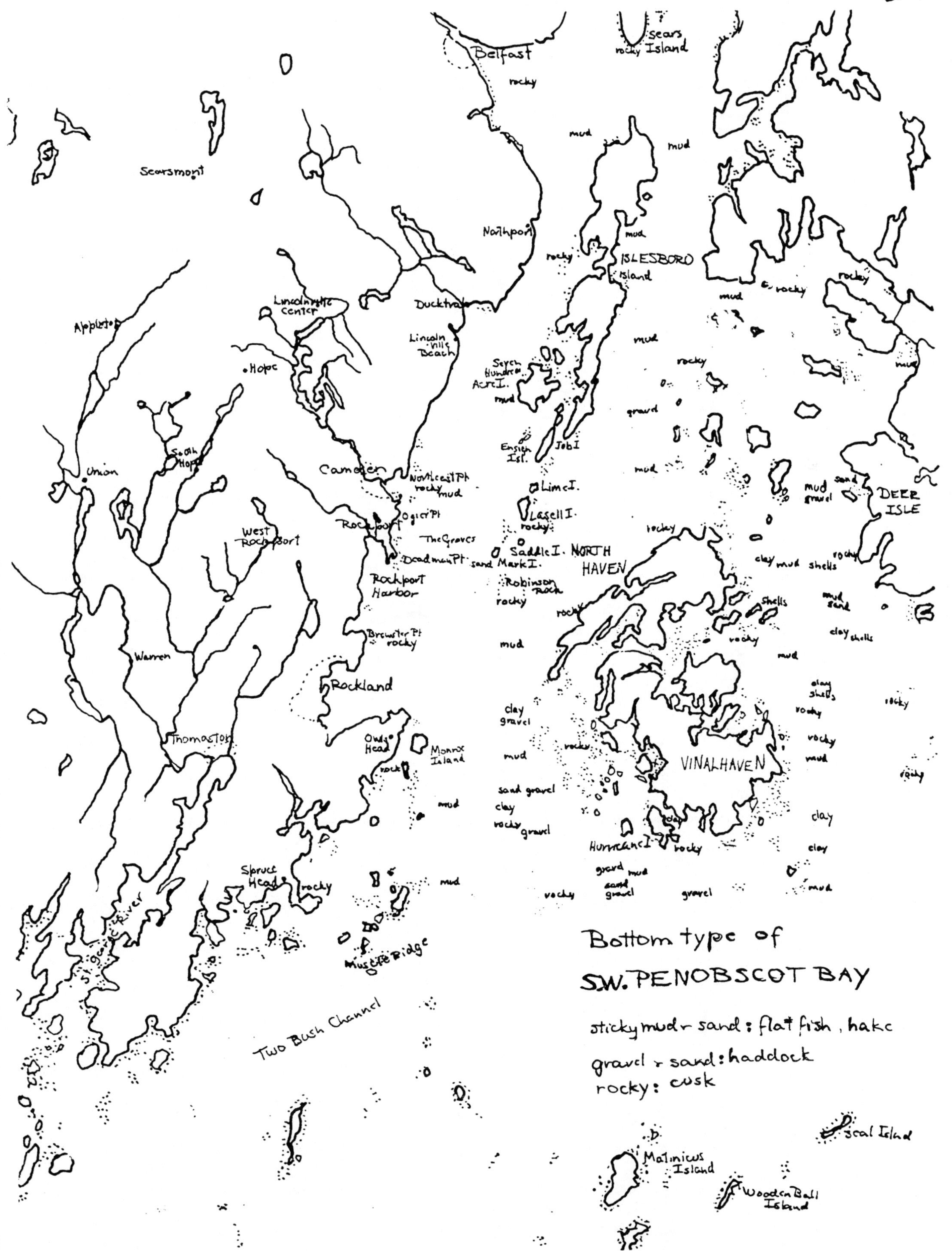

Belfast
Sears Island
rocky
Searsmont
Northport
ISLESBORO Island
Lincolnville Center
Ducktrap
Appleton
Lincolnville Beach
Hope
Seven Hundred Acre I.
South Hope
Union
Camden
Ensign Isl.
Job I.
Northeast Pt
Lime I.
Ogier Pt
Lasell I.
Rockport
The Graves
West Rockport
Saddle I.
NORTH HAVEN
Deadman Pt
Mark I.
Robinson Rock
Rockport Harbor
Brewster Pt
Warren
Rockland
Thomaston
Owls Head
Monroe Island
VINALHAVEN
Hurricane I.
DEER ISLE
Spruce Head
St. George River
Muscle Ridge
Two Bush Channel
Bottom type of
S.W. PENOBSCOT BAY
sticky mud & sand: flat fish, hake
gravel & sand: haddock
rocky: cusk
Seal Island
Matinicus Island
Wooden Ball Island
mud
sand
gravel
clay
shells

INSHORE-OFFSHORE FISH

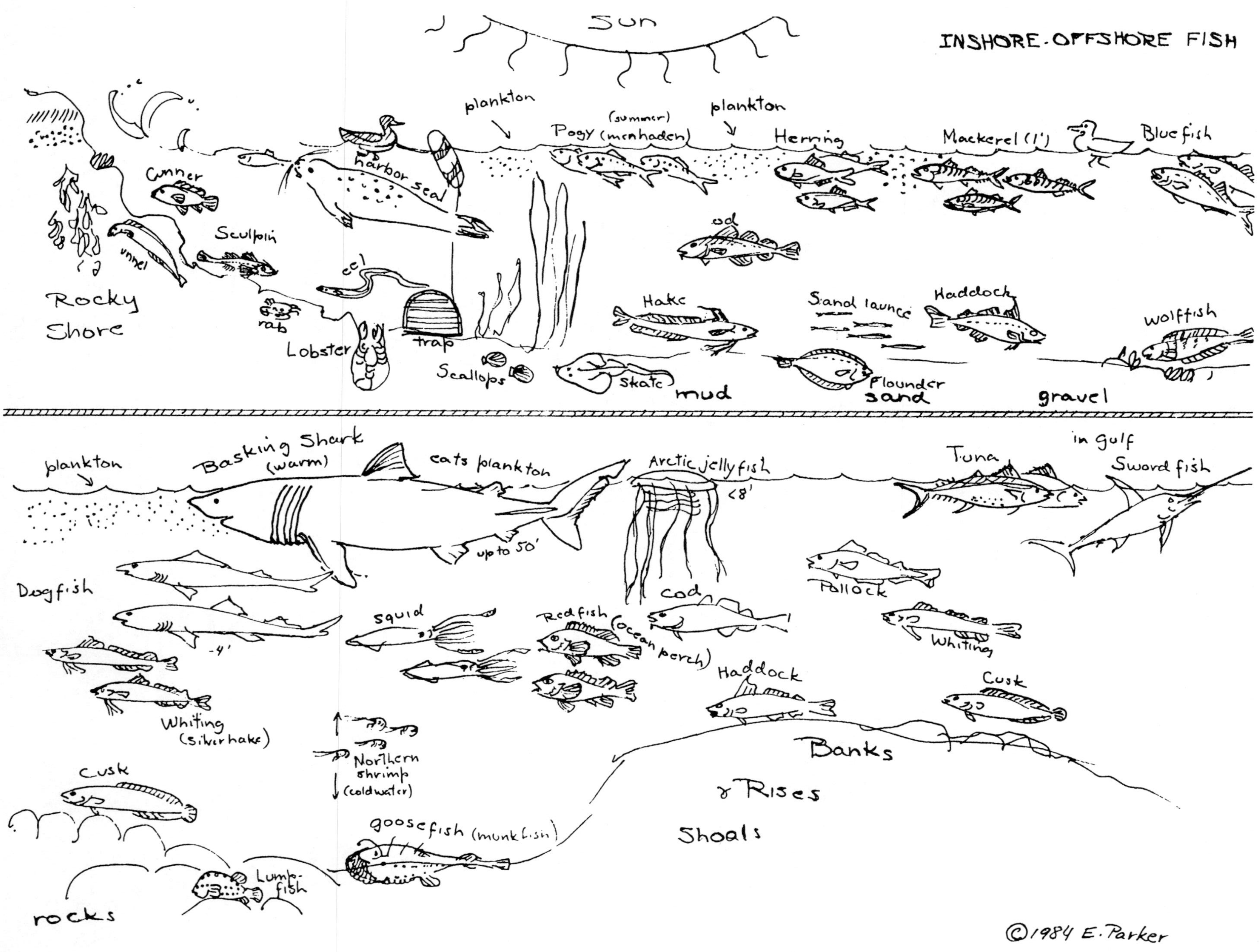

Sun

plankton

Pogy (menhaden) (summer)

plankton

Herring

Mackerel (1')

Bluefish

Cunner

harbor seal

Sculpin

cod

eel

Rocky Shore

crab

Lobster

trap

Scallops

Hake

Sand launce

Haddock

wolffish

skate

mud

Flounder

sand

gravel

plankton

Basking Shark (warm)

eats plankton

Arctic jellyfish <8'

Tuna

in gulf

Swordfish

up to 50'

Pollock

Dogfish

cod

squid

Redfish (ocean perch)

4'

Whiting

Haddock

Cusk

Whiting (silver hake)

Northern shrimp (coldwater)

Banks

Cusk

& Rises

Shoals

goosefish (monkfish)

Lumpfish

rocks

Large schools of herring and menhaden (pogy) live on the plankton that float near the surface of the water. This great body of plankton is the basis of life in the sea. The phytoplankton, tiny plants, many one-celled like diatoms, photosynthesize their food and must live near the sun's light on the surface. They are eaten by the zoo-plankton, (animal plankton) Protozoa, other simple animals, copepods, the tiny larvae of crabs, jellyfish, fish, etc. The herring schools come into the harbors in the

COD FAMILY

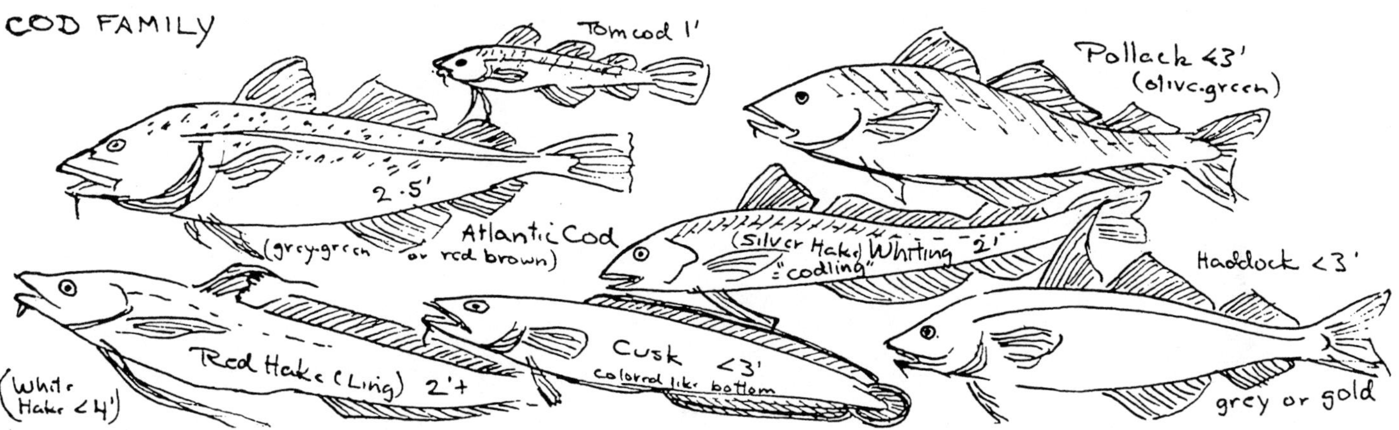

summer, showing as a fine ripple on the water and luminescent "firing" trails at night, as the phosphorescent plankton light up with their motion. The men-haden make a ripple like a light breeze, and nose out of the water. Mackerel schools come in the summer too, following tiny herring and krill (planktonic shrimp). These small fish are themselves pursued by cod, schools of voracious bluefish, squid, dogfish, pollack, whiting & striped bass.

Sea-going mammals also pursue the fish but don't venture into the dangerous harbor. The harbor seal, harbor porpoises and sometimes blackfish (pilot whales). The small fish are also devoured by sea birds – cormorant (shag), herring & blackback gulls, terns and guillemot. Some of these birds nest on small islands in the bay – their nests, eggs and guano covering the bare rocks. The winter

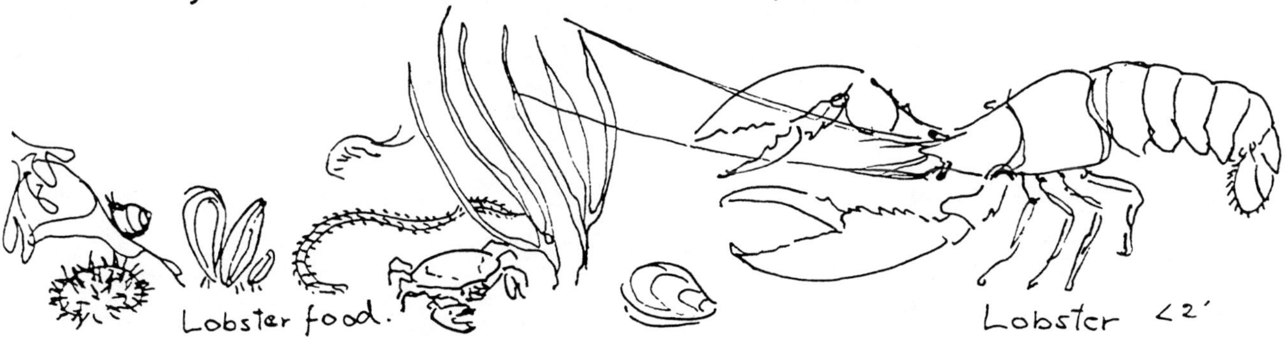

ducks that raft in the bays (eiders, old squaw, bufflehead, scoter, merganser) eat the bottom creatures and small fish. (see SALT MARSH) Some fish move in and out, inshore and offshore, north and south, according to the season. Although the temperature of the water is much more stable than the air temperature, especially the deeper water, the surface cools to near freezing in the winter. Menhaden, striped bass, bluefish only come north in the summer. Summer flounder and mackerel and herring come inshore in the summer. Most northern shrimp avoid warmer inshore summer temperatures, seeking colder waters offshore. Some fish spend part of their lives in fresh water, (anadromous fish). They swim up the rivers to spawn in running streams and lakes. These are the smelts, shad, alewives that come up the St. George River in the spring. Salmon run up Duck Trap in the fall. Lampreys go up the Penobscot.

Harbor Seal

Larger animals are feeding out in the waters of the Penobscot Bay and the Gulf of Maine. Occasionally, in the summer a huge basking shark drifts along with its mouth open, eating plankton like a baleen whale (a plankton-eating whale). Sometimes there are minke whales and even larger finback whales, among others. Red Arctic Jellyfish float along their long tentacles falling far below. They can grow as large as 8 feet but they all die in the winter;

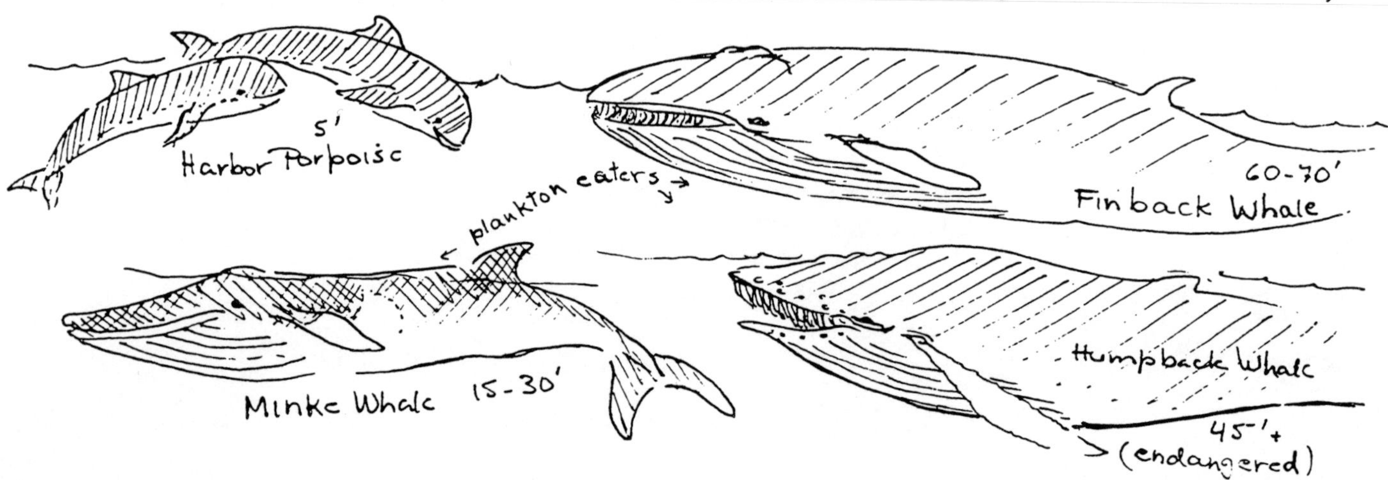

their offspring surviving in another form over the winter. Animals can grow to enormous size in the water without changing their form, because the water supports them. In comparison, large land animals need huge heavy bones to support their great weight

The little northern shrimp live out in the colder, deeper water eating plankton. The fishermen of our coast go out to catch them, and the fish that feed over the shoals and offshore banks. In the shallow offshore waters, there is more food for the fish because the seaweeds can photosynthesize nearer to the light.

The waters of the rivers, the Penobscot Bay, The Gulf of Maine and the Atlantic Ocean are generous to us in their gift of fish, seafood and sea weeds. The kind and amount of life in these waters varies with the water temperature, pollution and overfishing. The sea has been warming over the last generation, so there are fewer herring here and more menhaden than there used to be. The cold water shrimp sometimes disappear altogether. The occasional "red tides" of toxic plankton which make some of our shellfish dangerous to eat are partial to warm water.

Our shores are always in danger of oil spills from tankers and we are constantly letting oil escape from our boat engines and from our cars and trucks (crankcase oil usually ends up in the sea). If oil is pumped out of offshore sites, there will be even greater danger of serious oil spills affecting our coast.

Overfishing (taking too many creatures, and too small) may be so serious at times that it takes a population a long time to rebuild, if it can. We

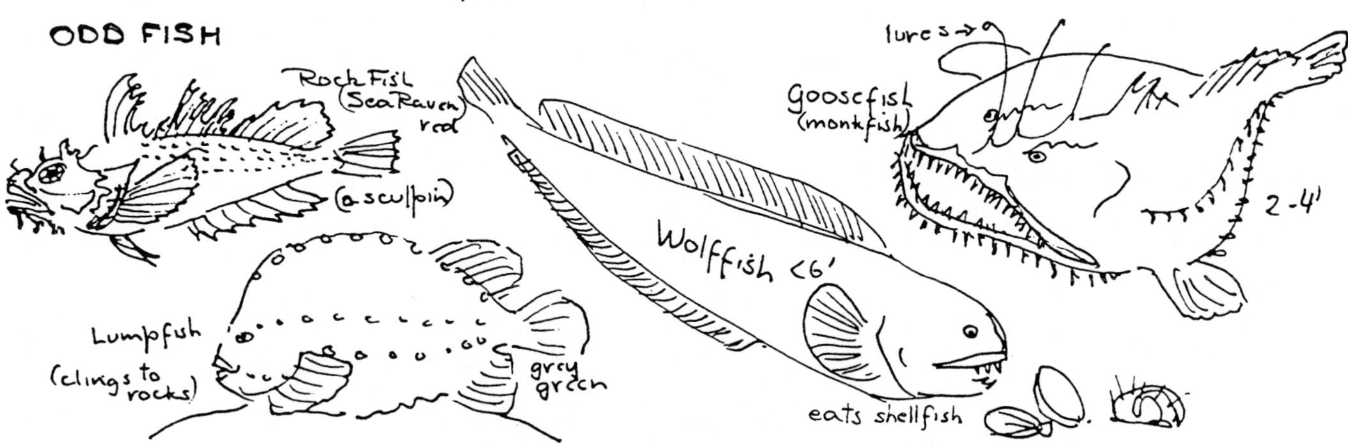

have overfished halibut, cod, haddock, winter flounder and shrimp in the past. We may be taking too many lobster. Lobsters and other bottom dwellers are also affected by the accumulation of synthetic gill nets fouling the bottom. Their rope does not rot as the old hemp did. There are also "ghost traps", lost traps that go on catching lobsters indefinitely on the bottom.

The fish that go up the river as part of their breeding cycle were stopped by the building of power dams in the 19th century. Many of these dams are gone now, and fish ladders have been built around some of them so that the alewife, smelt, salmon, shad can "climb" to their spawning grounds. But Meguntic ook still has some dams and only the the powerful eels can find their way around them.

We still do fish. Our lobstermen place their traps along the shore and some catch crabs off season. Some boats "drag" for scallops across the bay. Anglers fish from the docks in the summer. Fishermen still take smelt under the ice and salmon going up the Duck Trap river Eels are still trapped in the river. The Rockand boats go out for shrimp, and fish (cod, cusk, hake, flounder and red fish (ocean perch)) on Georges Bank, to be made into fish sticks at the packing company We still catch herring for sardines, bait, animal feed & fertilizer Clams are still dug on the flats of the St. George River. Until recently there were weirs here and there along the coast. And in summer 1979 a stop seine was rigged across Rockport Harbor to catch herring as in past years.

We are still the biggest predators in the sea.

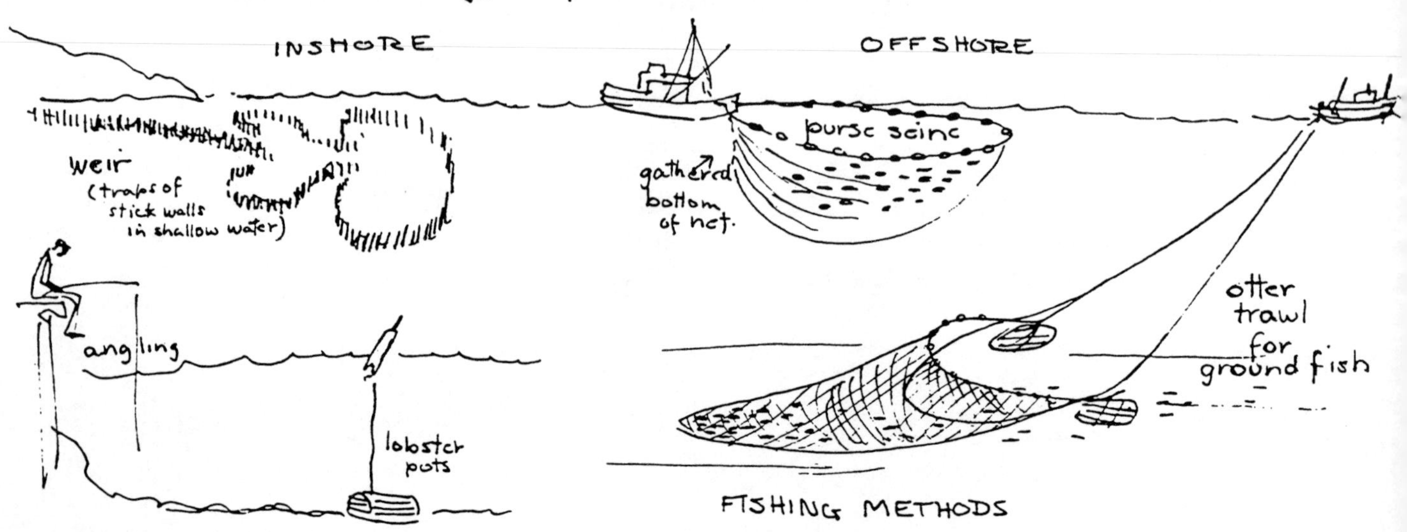

FISHING METHODS

FISHING CALENDAR (edible & potentially edible) – seasons

Month	Season	Deep water	Banks	Bay	Harbor	Rivers & Lakes
JAN.	winter			Crab; Scallops; shrimp		Smelts (ice fishing)
FEB.	winter			Crab; Scallops; shrimp		Smelts (ice fishing)
MAR.	winter	Cod	Herring	Crab; Scallops; shrimp		Smelts (ice fishing); alewives
APR.	spring	Cod	Herring	Lobster		alewives & shad on St. George
MAY	spring	Cod	Herring	Lobster; ("elvers" eel young heading up streams)		alewives & shad on St. George
JUNE	spring		Herring	Lobster; ("elvers" eel young heading up streams)	summer at the dock:	
JULY	summer	Tuna	Herring	herring & mackerel	pogey, herring, smelt	
AUG	summer	Swordfish	Herring	herring & mackerel	flounder, mackerel, cod, white perch	
SEPT	summer / fall	Cod	Herring	Lobster; herring & mackerel; (adult eel migrating back to)	dog fish, tomcod, eel	
OCT	fall	Cod		Lobster; (adult eel migrating back to)		Salmon in Ducktrap
NOV	fall	Cod		Lobster; (adult eel migrating back to)		Salmon in Ducktrap
DEC		Cod		Crab; scallops; shrimp		Salmon in Ducktrap

INSHORE–OFFSHORE YEAR-ROUND

- clams
- sea urchin (not spring)
- mussels
- dog fish
- skate
- eel
- lobster
- flounder
- cod
- pollack
- hake
- cusk
- herring
- redfish

available, but not necessarily in season

InShore - Offshore Food Web.

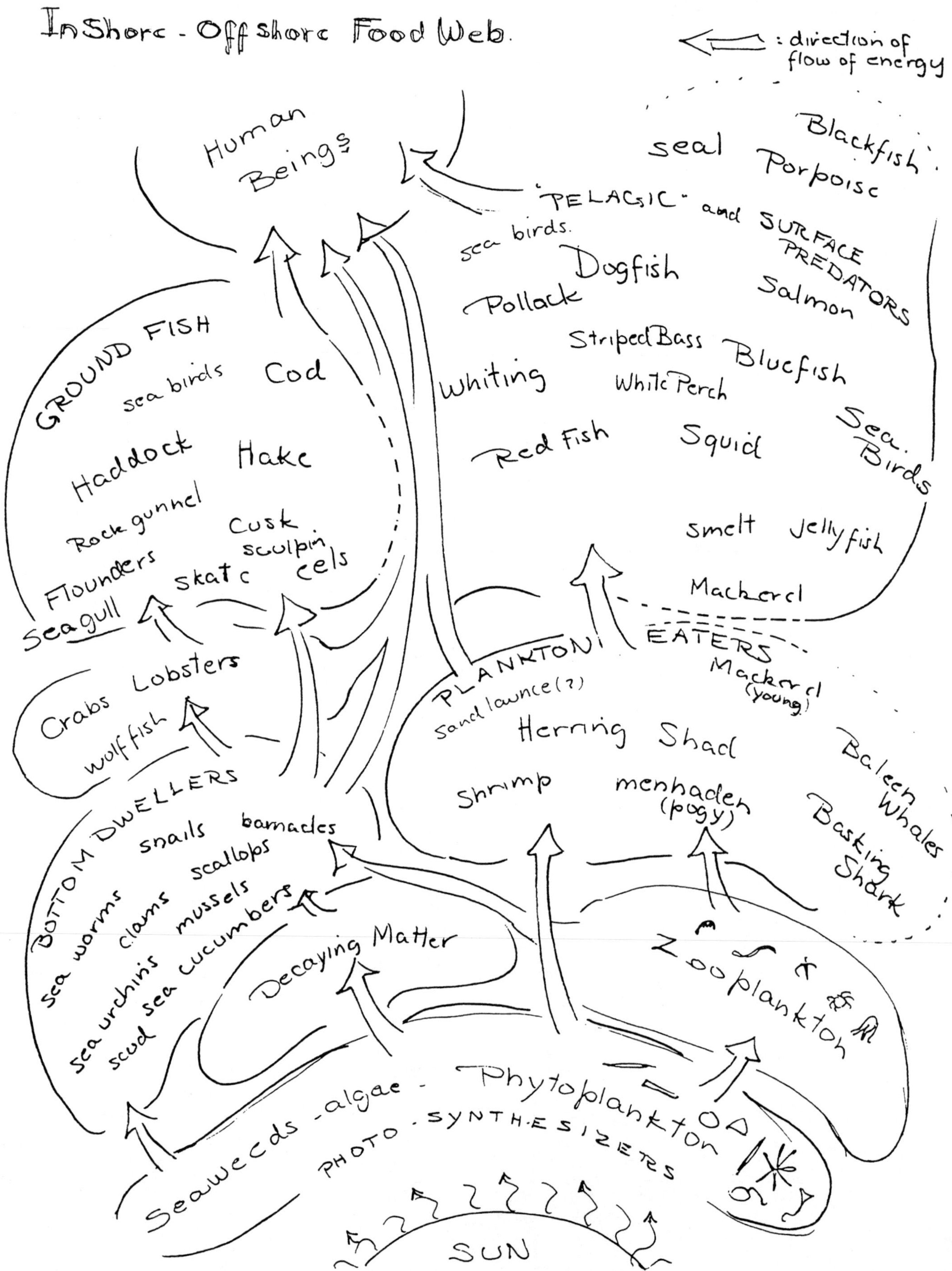

SALT MARSH

A salt marsh is an expanse of waving cord grasses and winding salt-water creeks that form at the shallow mouth of a river. It is sheltered from the waves of the open sea by rocky headlands or sand barriers. The marsh is fed by silt and nutrients washed along by the river and by the minerals brought in by the tides of the sea. Where the river meets the tide, it is slowed down, drops its load and a marsh is built.

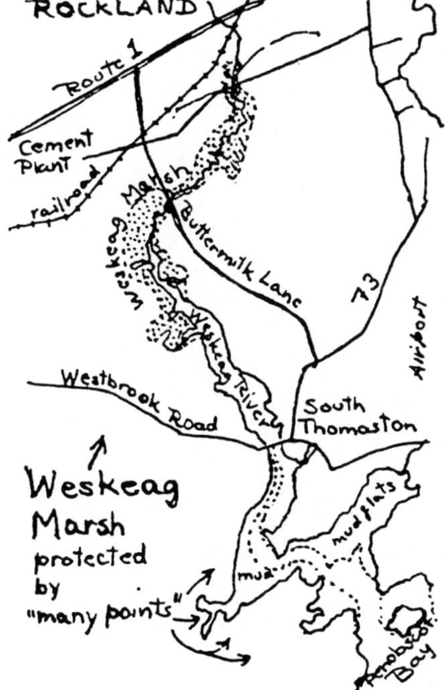

Weskeag Marsh protected by "many points"

There is one salt marsh near us, on the little Weskeag River in South Thomaston[1]. Further south the marshes are larger, but here the Maine coast is too rough and new to have much marsh-land. Not enough sediment washes off our rocky land and our river mouths are not sheltered enough.

When the silt in the river mouth, (estuary), is built up to a level where it is bared by the tide more than half the time, a coarse tall cordgrass (Spartina) begins to take hold. It slows the water further and holds the silt so the marsh builds up further. The river and the tides now wind through mud-banked creeks, a "brackish" mixture of salt and fresh water. There are pools in the marsh that are only connected to the creeks at high tide. And there are treacherous pond holes with "quick-sand" bottoms where the peat has rotted away.

Tall "thatch" cordgrass[2] lines the creek banks like a shaggy fringe. Just above it, in waving beds, is the smaller "salt hay" cordgrass.

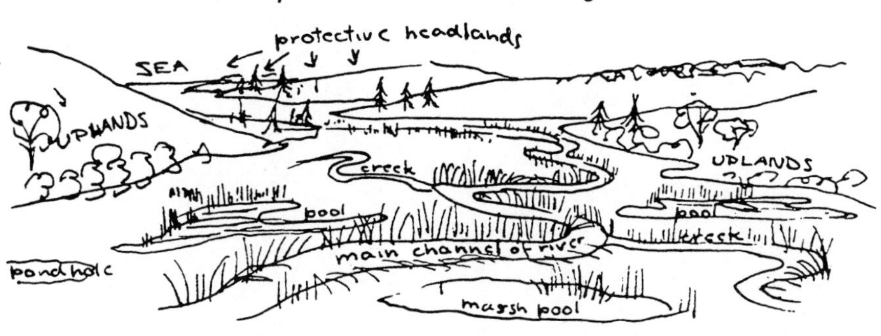

1. The name is shortened from 'Wessa Weskeag': "land of many points". It is also called the Waldo Tyler marsh, for the man who wrote many articles about the marsh.
2. Thatch grass was used by early colonists to thatch houses. The salt hay was harvested to feed cattle.

ALGAE - PHYTOPLANKTON (tiny floating plants)

x200
Blue green algae
x100
x700
x100
green algae
x300
x 90
Flagellates
x200
x200
Diatoms

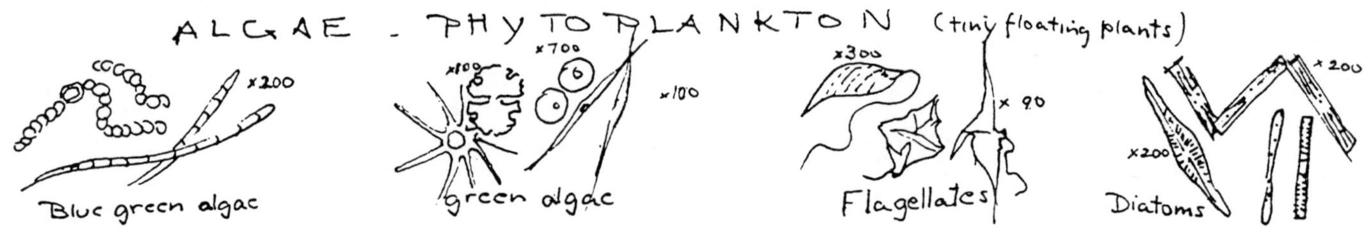

There are patches of wiry black rush and sweet grass higher above the tide. At the top of the marsh, the freshest part where the river enters, are cattails. Under the water, where the creeks empty, there is eelgrass, a real underwater flowering plant.

Tiny algae, bluegreen and green, live on the cordgrass and across the surface of the mud banks, giving them a greenish hue. Others float in the water and wash in and out with the tides. Mats of algae grow across the bottoms of the shallow pools, spongy and bubbly as they photosynthesize. The mats dry in lumpy curling crusts if there is little rain and the tides are not rising high. Tiny diatoms (plant plankton) hide in the mud at high tide and at night and come to the surface in daylight to catch the sunlight.

All these plants use the sunlight and the rich nutrients brought from the land and the sea to make food which is necessary for the life of the marsh. All other life depends on them. They are eaten alive and dead. They can produce 5 to 10 tons of "food" (organic matter) per acre, twice as much as good farmland. So there

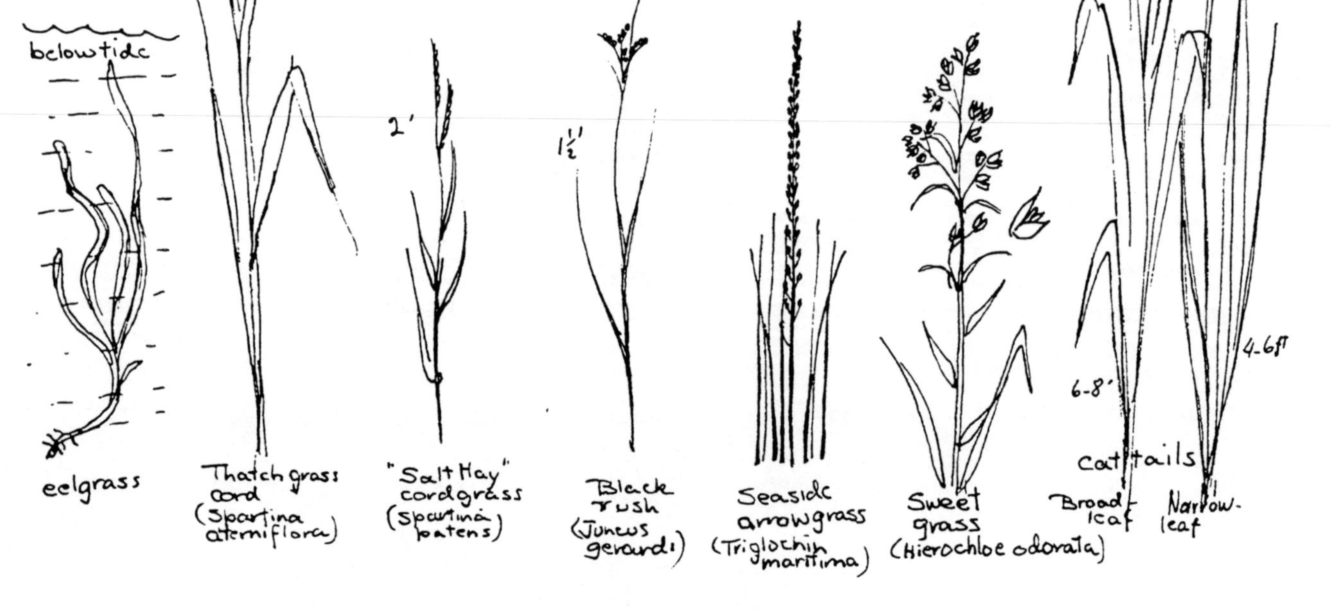

4-5'
below tide
2'
1½'
4-6ft
6-8'
eelgrass
Thatch grass cord (Spartina alterniflora)
"Salt Hay" cordgrass (Spartina patens)
Black rush (Juncus gerardi)
Seaside arrowgrass (Triglochin maritima)
Sweet grass (Hierochloe odorata)
cattails
Broad leaf
Narrow-leaf

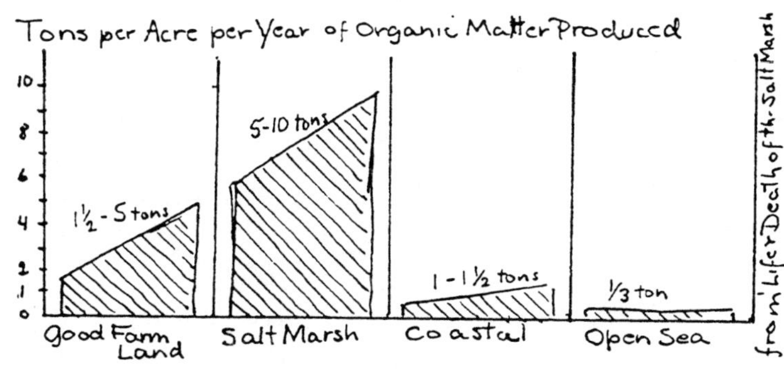

is plenty of food to support the many animals who live on the salt marsh.

The grasses are eaten by grasshoppers, crickets, sucking plant hoppers, grassfly larva, nematode worms in the roots. Grass seeds are eaten by sparrows, gold finch and mice. Further upland, the muskrat ate the cattails, before the muskrat were trapped out.

When the grass dies down in winter, it is broken and beaten down by the weather and tides and decomposed by bacteria. Decayed plant and animal bodies are mixed with the mineral rich mud by the moving waters to make a nutrient "soup" of detritus. The detritus and the algae that float and settle are consumed by other marsh animals who use a variety of filters and scoops to take in their food. Tiny protozoa, animal larva plankton and nematodes (roundworms) eat the algae and bacteria. Relatives of the earthworm and clam worm eat their way through the rich mud. Little snails (periwinkles, mud snails and marsh snails) scrape along the mud surface and up grass stalks, eating algae. Mosquito larvae eat detritus in the marsh pools and puddles. Mussels lie in the mud and pull detritus-filled water through their special filters when the tide is in, building up great hummocks in the marsh with the wastes they deposit. Some fish are detritus eaters too.

The marsh is full of life during the bright, warmer months. It is full of animals that have come to eat the detritus-eaters and the grass eaters.

There are spiders, predatory bugs, robberflies and dragonflies. Marsh wrens, swamp and savannah sparrows, red-wing blackbirds and swallows eat insects too. The voracious larvae of the deerfly and marsh fly wriggle through the mud and

plant hopper
longhorn grasshopper
marsh snail eating algae
cordgrass
grass fly larva
nematodes in roots

WATER BIRDS IN THE WESKEAG - MARSH, SHORES & BAYS

YEAR ROUND
herring gull
black duck
loon
eider duck

SPRING and FALL BIRDS migrating through
Canada goose . Bonapart gull . . G.W. teal . greater & lesser yellowlegs . snipe . plover . sandpipers .

SUMMER BIRDS
B.W. Teal . Great Blue Heron . bittern
rail . snowy egret . Woodcock . killdeer .
kingfisher . sharp shin hawk - osprey

WINTER BIRDS
mallard
golden eye
purple sandpiper
old squaw
bufflehead
merganser
(sea ducks) in open water

Jan. Feb. Mar. Apr. May June July Aug. Sept Oct. Nov. Dec.

eat other small animals. Small, shrimp-like crustaceans or "scud" (amphipods), catch tinier animals in the pools and on the mud. Sharp-tailed sparrows run mouse-like through the grass, eating the sandhoppers: Little mummichog fish and sticklebacks eat mosquito larvae in the pools. Raccoon come to the marsh to dig clams, catch fish and little green crabs. Mink and otter come too. Bigger fish come swimming in with the tide to eat smaller water animals: (flounder, codling, tommy cod smelt, eels).

Sharp-tailed Sparrow down in the grass, catching sand shrimp (amphipods)

Great numbers of birds come to the marsh to feed. They come up the coast in the spring, (May & June), following the greening grasses and settling to feed in the pools and reeds. First come the Canada geese, followed by many others: blue-winged teal*, mallard, merganser (all ducks) plover, yellowlegs, sandpiper, dowitcher, snipe*, willet, godwit, rail*, great blue heron*, green heron*, snowy egret, bittern*, kingfisher*, terns and gulls. Some settle in the marsh for the summer and nest there (* marks nesting birds). Others go on to places farther north. As the days grow shorter in the late summer and fall (August through November), they make their way south again, feeding as they go. Some northern birds follow to winter in our marsh and out in the bays: golden eye ducks ("whistlers") and

All these birds have long pointed beaks to poke down in the mud and grab worms and crustaceans.

bufflehead, mallard ducks and mergansers. And some birds stay year round, as the herring gull and the black ducks.

These birds gather their food in different ways. The dabbling ducks (black duck, teal and mallard) paddle in the ponds and "bottom up" to scoop plants and occasional animals from the pool bottoms with their wide bills. The diving ducks swim under the deeper, open water to catch fish and crustaceans (goldeneye, mergansers & sea ducks). Many shore birds (sandpipers, godwit, yellowlegs, willet etc) have long pointed beaks that they can drive down into the mud or pool bottom at low tide to pull out worms, molluscs, and small burrowing shrimp (scud again). The great blue heron fish in the pools with their sharp long beaks.

Sometimes a hawk hovers above the marsh: sharpshin, Cooper's or broad-wing. Down nearer the sea and open water there are osprey watching for fish. Crows and gulls feed on the marsh and scavenge the leavings of other animals. Bonapart gulls fly in from the bay.

The grasses and algae are not the only plants in the marsh.

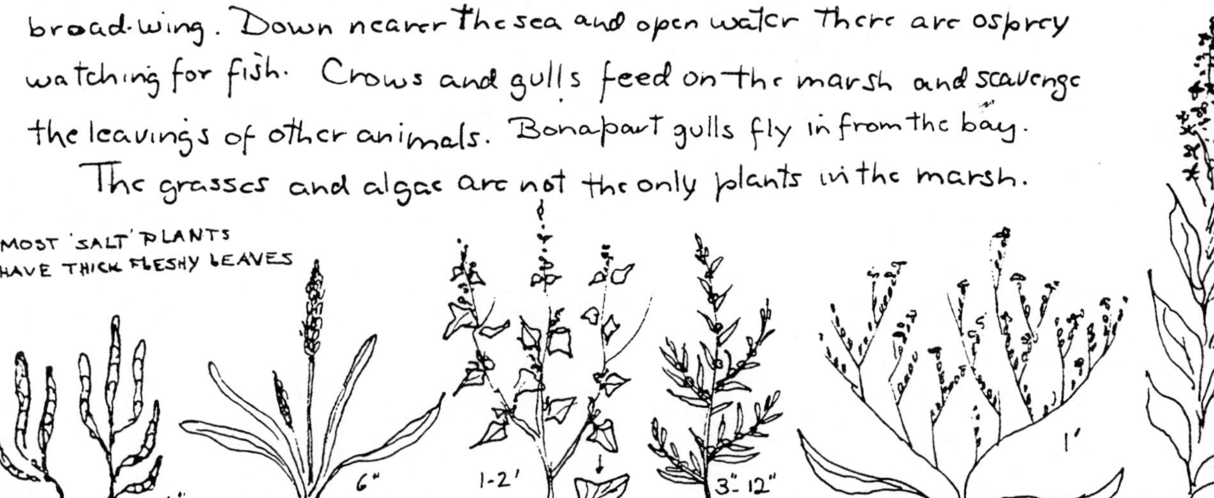

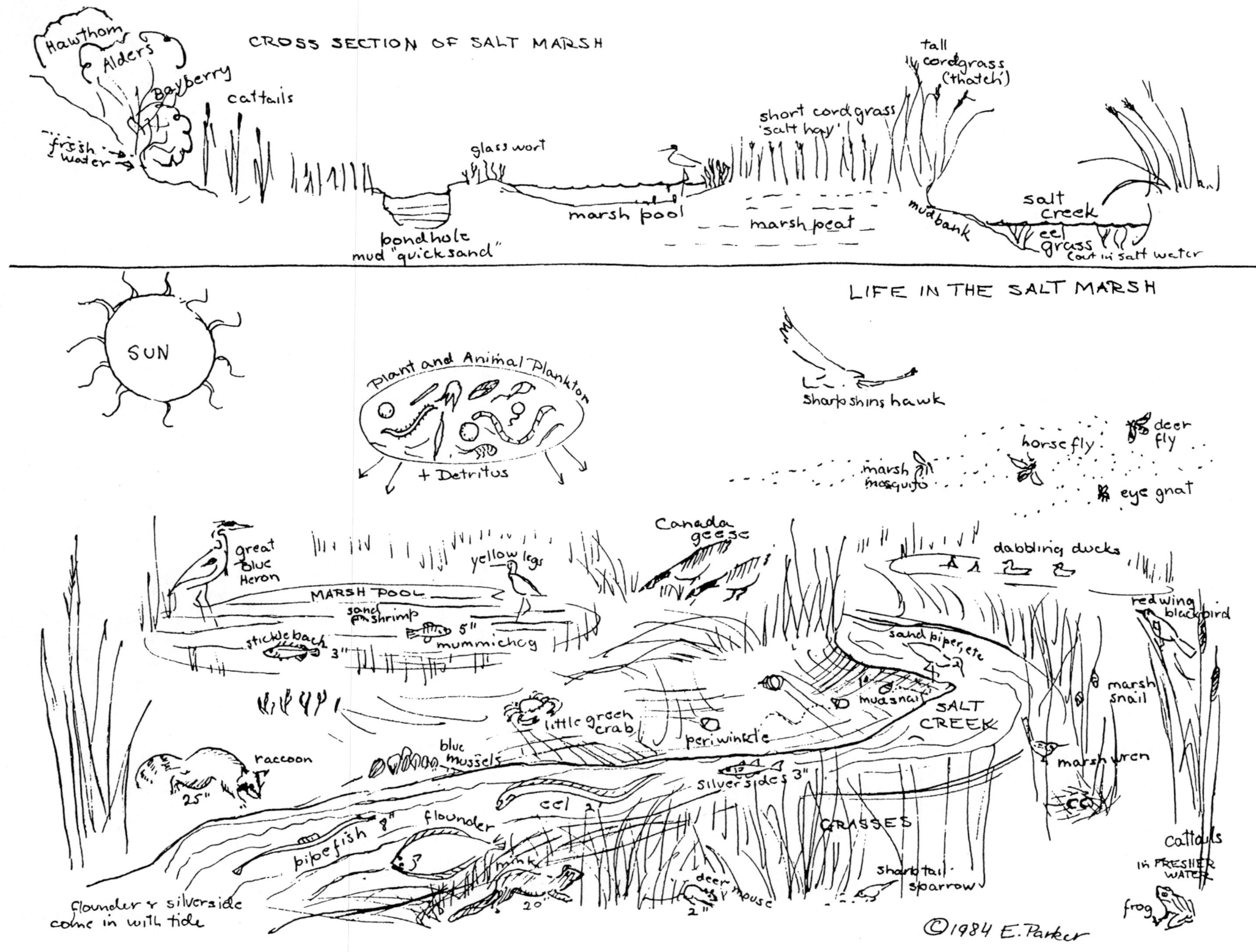
CROSS SECTION OF SALT MARSH
Hawthorn
Alders
Bayberry
cattails
fresh water
glass wort
pondhole
mud "quicksand"
marsh pool
short cordgrass
'salt hay'
marsh peat
tall cordgrass
('thatch')
mudbank
salt creek
eel grass
(cut in salt water
LIFE IN THE SALT MARSH
SUN
Plant and Animal Plankton
+ Detritus
Sharpshins hawk
deer fly
horsefly
marsh mosquito
eye gnat
Canada geese
great blue Heron
yellow legs
MARSH POOL
sand shrimp
5"
mummichog
stickleback
3"
dabbling ducks
redwing blackbird
sand piper, etc
mudsnail
SALT CREEK
marsh snail
little green crab
periwinkle
blue mussels
raccoon
25"
silversides 3"
marsh wren
eel
flounder
pipefish 8"
GRASSES
mink
20"
deer mouse
2"
sharptail sparrow
cattails
in FRESHER WATER
frog
flounder & silverside
come in with tide
©1984 E. Parker

There are the stubby glass worts on the saltier parts, with thick, fleshy little branches. They turn a beautiful red in the fall, giving patches of color to the fading marsh. There is yellow seaside goldenrod and delicate seaside lavender, yellow vetchling and silver weed. Seaside plantain (goose tongue), and orach are edible, and glass worts were once made into pickles.

On the upland edges of the marsh are bayberry, alders, hawthorn and poison ivy.

Always the tide goes in and out of the marsh, drawn twice a day by the moon. The plants and animals of the marsh must have special ways of living with the constantly changing water level and the varying concentrations of salt and oxygen. The cord grass can survive because of its high internal salt level and little glands that excrete extra salt. It has airpassages that carry oxygen down to its roots and help provide oxygen to organisms in the airless mud. Sometimes a marsh pool is cut off from the tides and dries out; the salt becomes so concentrated that nothing but a few bacteria can live there.

Many muddwellers need to stay wet, so when the tide goes out, they go with it, or bury themselves in the mud, or close up as do mussels and barnacles. Some animals must stay dry and breathe air, so they leave the marsh, on foot or wing, or they climb up the grass stalks as do the marsh snails. Nothing that cannot cope with the tides and salt of the marsh can live there, and still it is the richest kind of land.

Until recently, salt marshes were not considered valuable by town people. Indians have always used the marshes for hunting and gathering. Early colonists used the grass for thatch and hay. Our own hunters and birdwatchers know the value of the marsh. But during the last 150 years, we have been dumping garbage in marshes, polluting the rivers that run through them, and trying to fill them in to build houses as fast as we can. The animals are overhunted and overtrapped.

But now we are beginning to remember the value of the marshes. We have learned how much more productive they are than other kinds of land. We know that many important fish (2/3 of the commercial catch) come into the marsh during some part of their life cycle: some to spawn in the marsh, some to spend a sheltered childhood, some to feed during the summer (flounder, smelt, codling, sculpin.) The marsh feeds them all. We cannot lose the marshes without losing the fish.

With this new understanding, in 1967 the State of Maine passed a law requiring anyone wanting to change a marsh to obtain a permit. Permits are difficult to get and this protects the marsh. The state also has a program to buy valuable wetlands in order to protect them from development. The Weskeag is partly owned by the state. In the past, the cement plant in Thomaston (see map) scattered white lime dust over the whole region, choking the vegetation and animals of the marsh. In 1972, "scrubbers" were installed in compliance with new air pollution laws, and not as much dust comes from the plant now.

But all the measures of the government will not be enough to protect this resource unless we all know its value and are willing to keep it.

Bonapart gull 12-14"

1. The Weskeag is too short and small a river to have fish running up it to spawn in fresh water.

SALT MARSH FOOD WEB

MUD FLATS and SANDY BEACHES

Mud flats are formed in shallow bays where the water currents are slowed enough to deposit fine mud particles and the waves cannot beat in to carry it away. Mud flats are sheltered from the direct force of the sea by protective points of land, but they are not protected enough to permit grasses to grow and build up sod as in the salt marshes. They are swept bare by the tides and nothing shelters the creatures that live there but the mud itself. Such animals must burrow into the mud for shelter and to stay moist while the tide is out.

The soft surface of the mud at low tide has a thin scum of dark greenish plant plankton, diatoms and blue green algae. These tiny plants photosynthesize food which is consumed by animals. Several inches below the surface lies a black, airless layer, colored by the purple, sulphur-based, photosynthesizing bacteria that can live without oxygen. The creatures that live in the mud, mostly worms and molluscs, must get their oxygen and food from the water above when the tide is in. They cannot filter their food if they live in very fine mud because the filters would become clogged by the tiny mud particles, so they either eat their way through the mud like earthworms or create a current in their burrows to wash the food through. The animals that live in a sandier area, however, can filter food with out clogging because the sand particles are larger.

We have at least two mudflats nearby - Sherman's Cove and Clam Cove (at Glen Cove). Clam Cove is closed to clam digging because of pollution but Sherman's Cove recently reopened to diggers with a town permit. Ducktrap, north of Lincolnville Beach is still open and clam diggers still go out on the St. George River flats near Thomaston.

In Clam Cove, part of the flat is muddy and part more sandy so you will find different creatures according to the amount of sand. On the surface of the

mud flat, you will see the tracks of little mudsnails (Nassa), and periwinkles winding over the mud ripples scavenging what they can. There are clumps of blue mussels, clinging together and anchored as best they can to the few stones near the edge. Some barnacles live on the mussel shells. On the sandier portions, there are sometimes moon snail "sand collars" (1) revealing the presence of the fierce moon snail who can dig inches down to attack a clam. Below the surface of the flat there are soft shell clams, their finger-size holes showing on the surface. These holes squirt when you step nearby. A large wedge-shaped hole may be made by a razor clam - also very good to eat. On the sandier parts, there are usually more razor clams, and at lowest water, there are some big hen clams

You may see many other mysterious holes and bumps in the mud, all clues to what lies below. Some belong to different kinds of annelid worms (like earthworms), that stick their heads out to feed when the tide is high. The lugworm (Arenicola) makes a pile of castings at the mouth of its burrow. The ornate worm (Amphitrite) has a little volcano-shaped mound at the top of its burrow. Little groups of straw-sized chimneys sticking up mean that there are bamboo worms (Clymenella) underneath. A black dime-sized smudge on the flat may mean that a trumpet worm lives below (Cistenides). The point of its "trumpet" casing may stick up above the mud surface - or you might find the empty case, cone shaped and made of sand particles. Bits of waving shell or seaweed in shallow water may mean that decorator worms (Diopatra) are underneath. Another worm that lives in the mudflat is the clam worm (Nereis) that comes out at high tide and swims around to catch its food. Some people dig clam worms to use for bait. They can bite painfully.

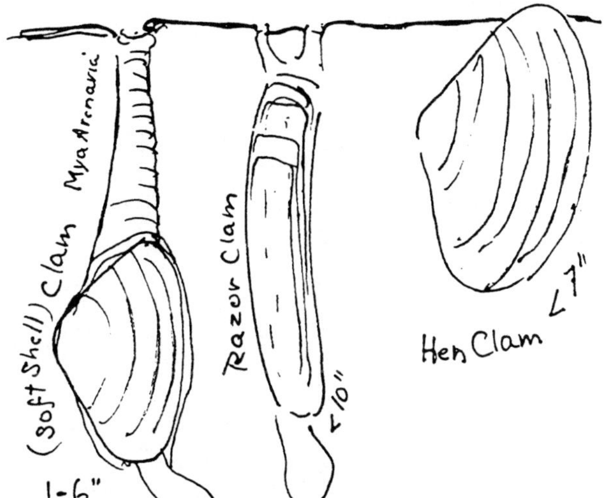

(1) These "sand collars" are actually egg cases of the moon snail.

MUD FLATS and Worms

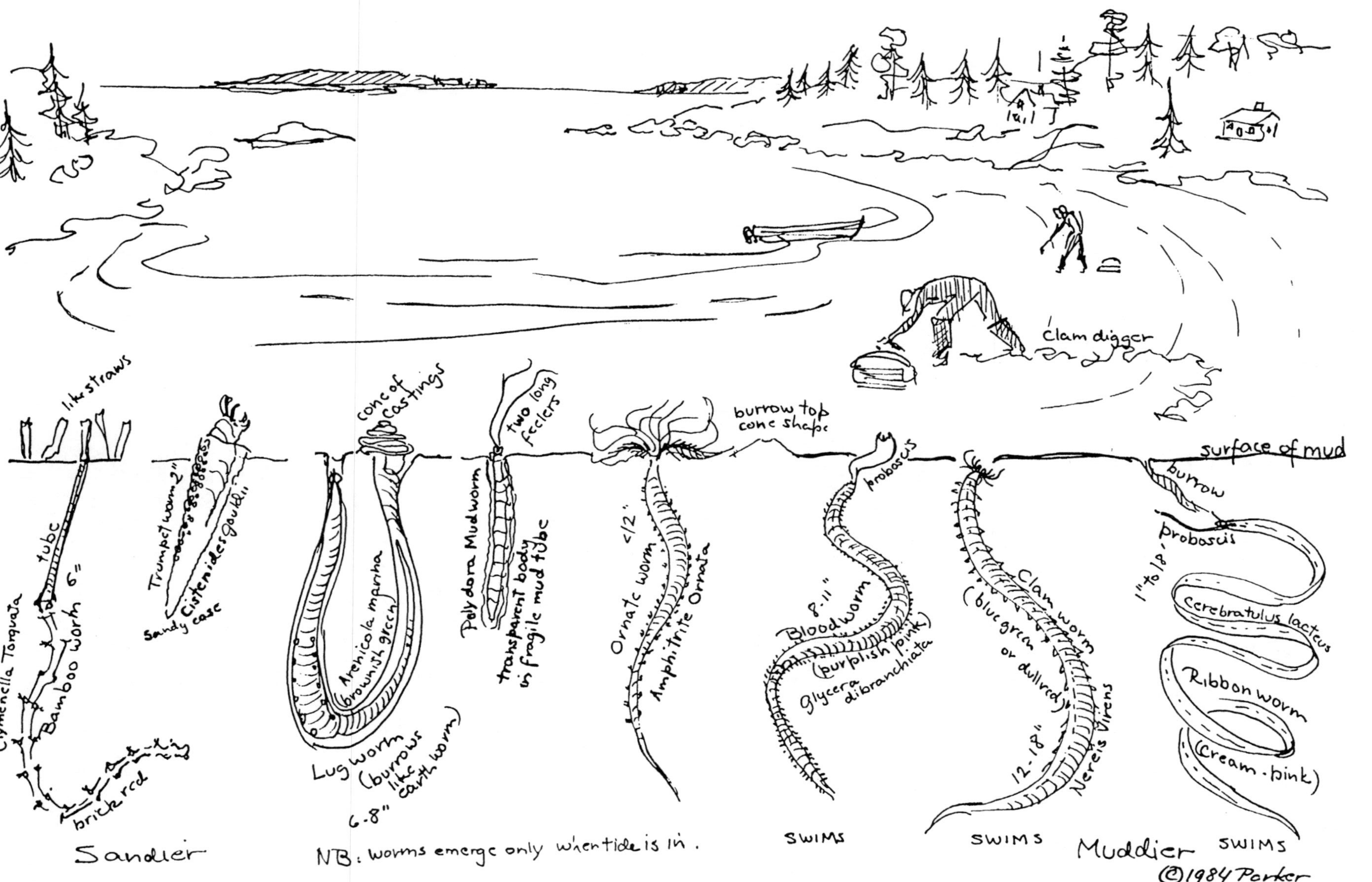

Digging about, you might find purple-pink blood worms (Glycera), which are also dug for bait, and the simple ribbon worms (Cerebratulus), long, flat, pale things that can also swim when the tide is in. They also can grow enormously long, to 18 feet.

There are few larger plants on the mud flat – a bit of rockweed here and there clinging to a stone or clump of mussels. Below the low tide level, there may be some sea weed, such as Enteromorpha intestinalis. Eel grass used to grow here, in groves in the shallow water, but it was killed by a disease in 1931-32 and is only now beginning to grow back on this coast. Eel grass is actually a flowering plant that lives as a seaweed and harbors a whole community of creatures such as sand dollars, stickleback, pipefish. The loss of the eel grass means that the mudflats have become less stable, less sheltered so fewer animals, including clams, can live there.

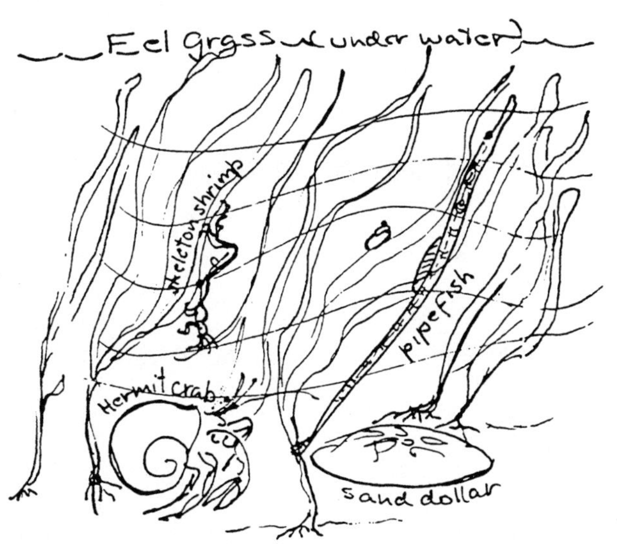

The mudflats are visited by scavenging people and herring gulls and by migratory shore birds (see calendar in "Salt Marsh" section). When the tide is up, fish swim in to hunt the worms and molluscs: flounder, skate, sculpin, silversides and others. In the winter, rafts of sea ducks, (eider, bufflehead, old squaw, scoter and black duck) with an occasional loon and coot, float over the shallow bays and off the rocky shore, diving for their food. (The black duck dabbles for weeds and shellfish and crustaceans.

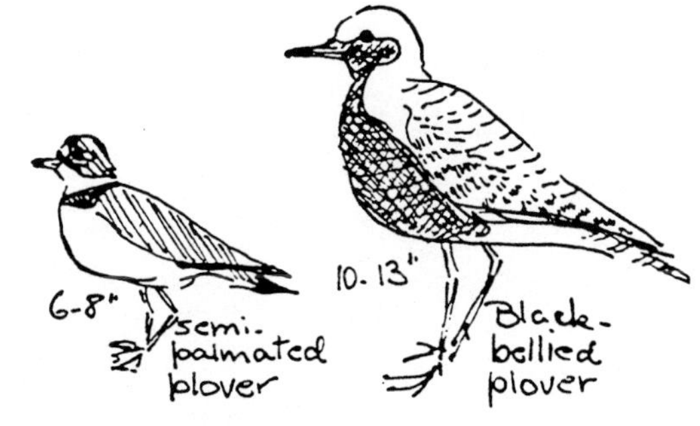

Some spring shore birds

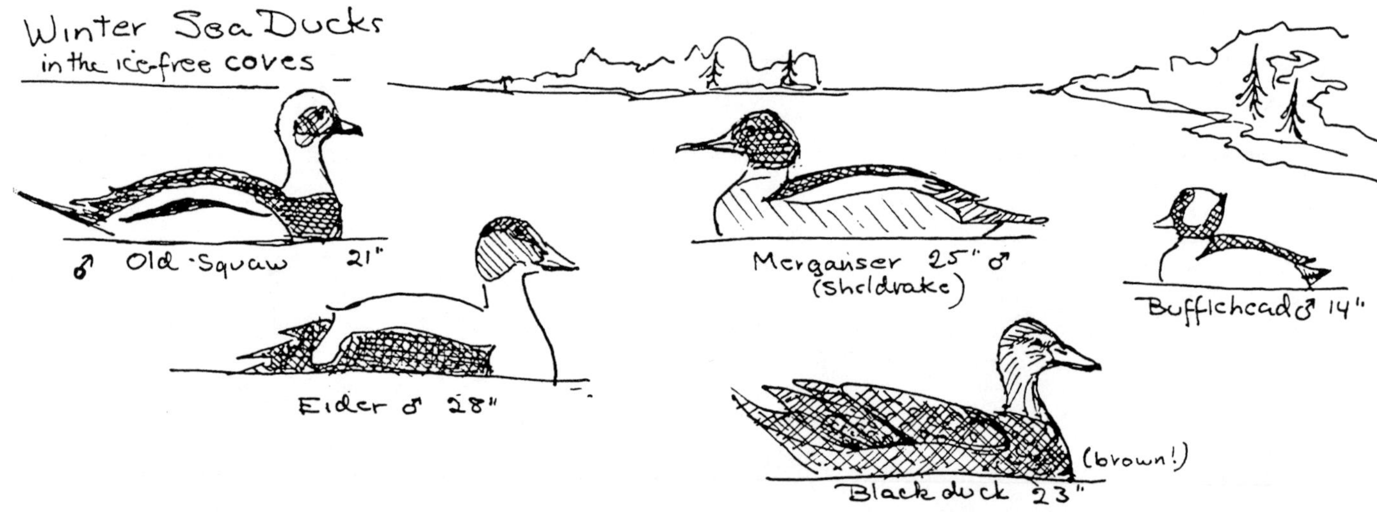

We have very few sandy beaches in our area. Lincolnville Beach and the Camden Public Beach and a few tiny private beaches. Here the particles are bigger and harder (mostly quartz) because these places are slightly steeper and more exposed to wave action than the mud flats. Here sea weeds are washed up by storms and high tides to form several windrows winding along the beach. In the piles of drying and decaying weed you will find hopping sand fleas (Orchestra) that scatter as you probe, reacting as they would to a long beaked shore bird. There are bits of crab carapace, sea urchin skeletons, fish vertebrae, pieces of clam & mussel shell, periwinkles, an occasional big horse mussel shell, a chunk of white coral-like algae, a skate egg case, a bit of dead man's fingers sponge. The seaweeds are mostly knotted wrack with an occasional strand of kelp.

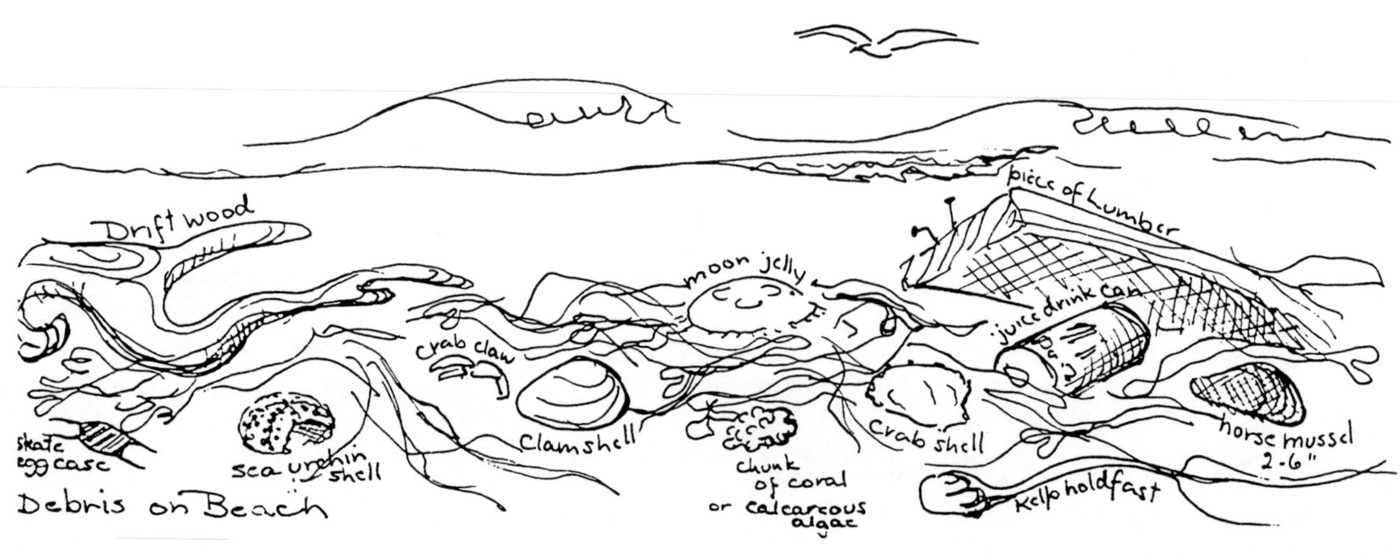

Debris on Beach

MUD FLATS

Mud flats are very sensitive to pollution by human wastes. The water currents are not strong enough to flush them clean. When sewage from near-by houses and moored boats in the bays empties into the water, the human bacteria or viruses in the wastes are harbored in the creatures of the mud flats that absorb the wastes as they eat. The germs are then taken in by humans who dig and eat the clams from the flats. For this reason the Department of Marine Resources must close the flats to protect people from their own wastes. As we learn to take care of our sewage properly, we are again able to harvest clams again from these flats.

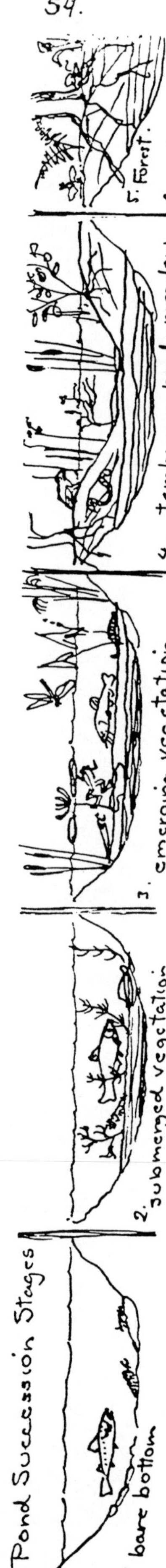

FRESHWATER and WETLANDS

When the glaciers retreated, the land below was left pock-marked with lakes, ponds and little depressions filled with water (1). During 10-12 thousand years, these watery places have gradually filled with eroded silt and sand, and matted vegetation. Ponds have become shrubby swamps and wet patches of forest. Rock-bottomed lakes have become shallower and mud-bottomed. Reed marshes have inched out from the shores. So we have a range of wet lands (2): tiny mountain top bogs, the great Oyster River Bog, swamps of cedar or red maple, alder and willow swales, sedge and reed marshes along the edges of lakes, and the lakes and ponds themselves.

The acid bogs are poorly drained (see Bog section) but the other wetlands are charged and drained by springs and the flow of streams: fast rushing forest streams and small flowing rivers like the Megunticook and the Goose River. The movement of the water joins all the lands, moving from the sky, through the land, to the sea and back again. The plants and animals that live in these wet habitats are united by the water that flows through them. One habitat blends with another: the lake turns into swamp which turns into forest. The fast stream flows into the lake which empties into the slow stream, and so on.

These living places are teeming with plants and animals of all shapes and sizes, but because of the wetness, we don't always see much of them. One way to look at wetland plants and animals is from a slow canoe, paddled along the edge of a pond, looking down at the bottom and scooping stuff out to look more closely. Wading in is good, too.

Different associations of plants and animals live in wet places

(1) see map of Wetlands

(2). Wet places to visit: Bog Bridge, Barrets Cove, Goose River (golf course), Fernald Neck, off road on Beauchamp Pt.

according to their need for light, oxygen, pH (acidity), heat, type of bottom, speed of water and amount of nutrients. A fast-flowing rocky ⓐ mountain stream is cold, has plenty of oxygen & few nutrients. It is hard for living things to avoid being washed away by the current. Blue-green algae live in the fast stream, with dark mosses (fountain moss) and some insect larvae that can cling to the rocks or crawl under them. The spring blackfly larvae cement themselves onto boulders in the rushing water, looking like a mat of dark moss. They sweep tiny diatom algae cells into their mouths.

FAST STREAM

Where the stream slows a bit ⓑ, there is gravel, and then sand, on the bottom, and more life. Some water weeds can root and worms (nematodes, bristleworms and flatworms) may find shelter along with many insect nymphs & larvae that crawl about eating plant and animal matter. Sponges and bryozoans coat the sheltering undersides of stones. The caddisfly larvae make themselves heavy sand cases, to weight themselves down as they crawl about, eating

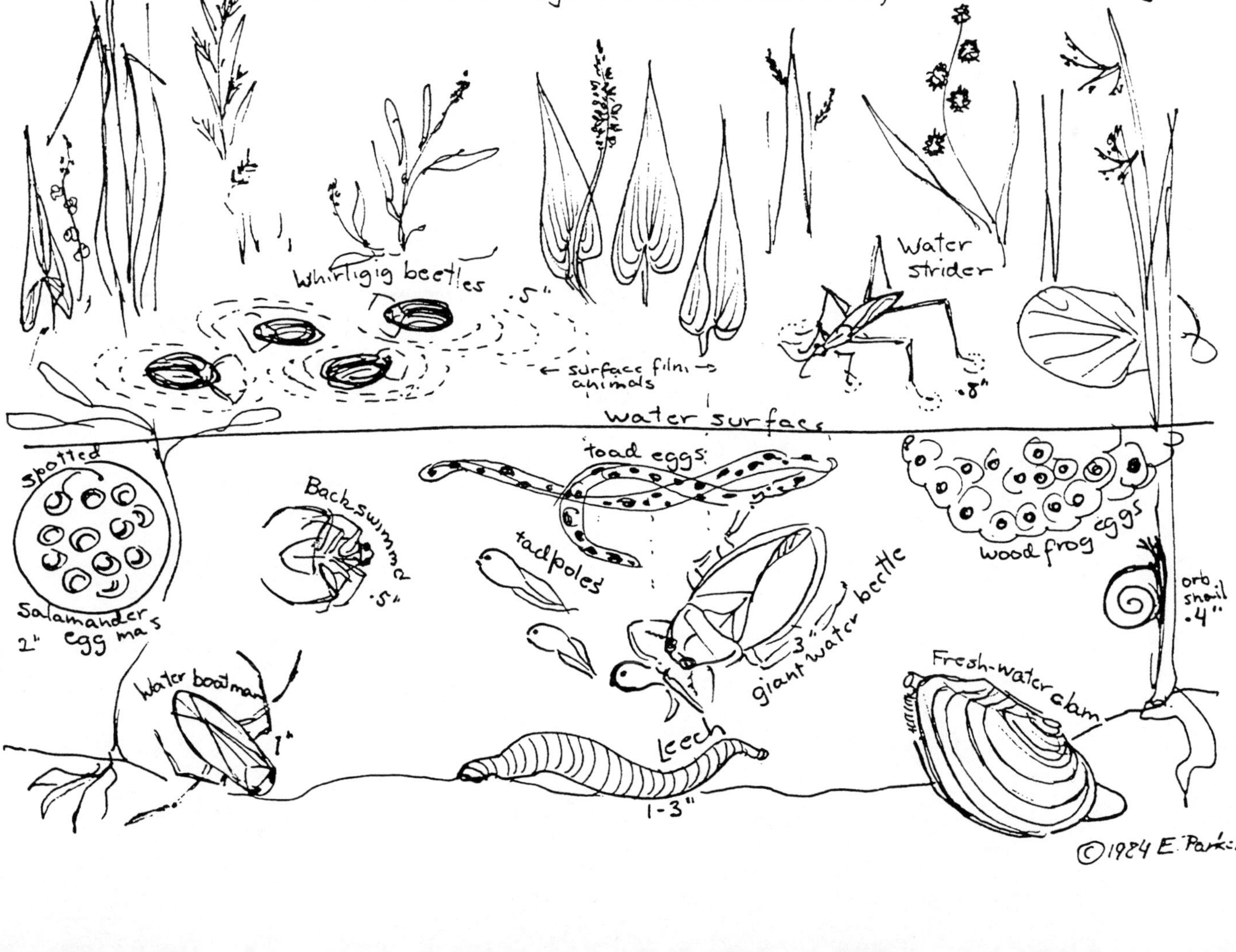

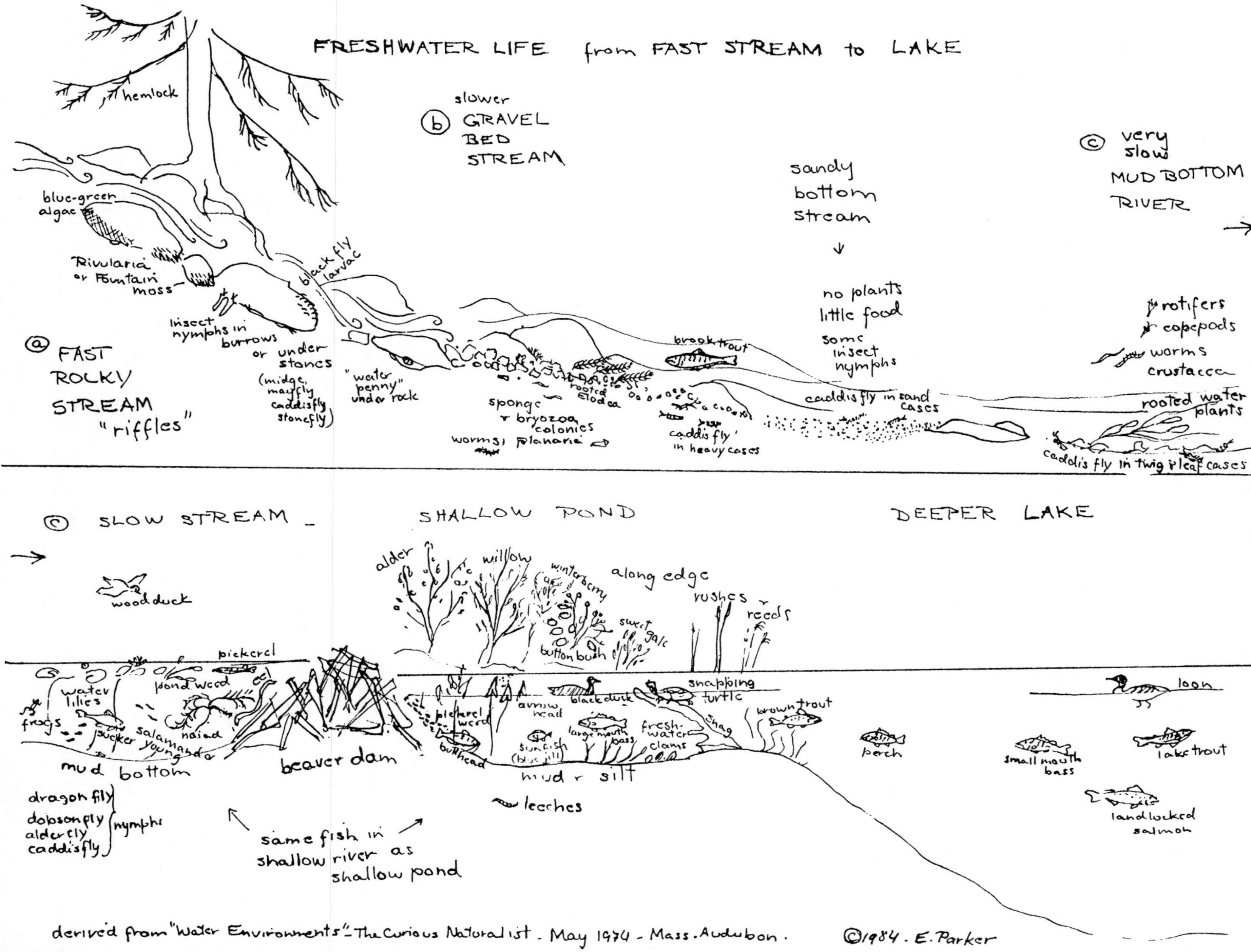
FRESHWATER LIFE from FAST STREAM to LAKE
hemlock
blue-green algae
Rivularia or Fountain moss
black fly larvae
insect nymphs in burrows or under stones (midge, mayfly, caddisfly, stonefly)
ⓐ FAST ROCKY STREAM "riffles"
slower ⓑ GRAVEL BED STREAM
"water penny" under rock
sponge & bryozoa colonies
worms, planaria
rooted Elodea
brook trout
caddis fly in heavy cases
sandy bottom stream
no plants little food
some insect nymphs
caddis fly in sand cases
ⓒ very slow MUD BOTTOM RIVER
rotifers
copepods
worms
crustacea
rooted water plants
caddis fly in twig & leaf cases
ⓒ SLOW STREAM – SHALLOW POND DEEPER LAKE
wood duck
pickerel
water lilies
pond weed
eel
frogs
sucker
salamander young
naiad
mud bottom
dragon fly
dobsonfly
alderfly
caddisfly
nymphs
beaver dam
same fish in shallow river as shallow pond
alder
willow
winterberry
along edge
rushes & reeds
sweet gale
button bush
pickerel weed
arrow head
black duck
snapping turtle
bullhead
sunfish (blue gill)
largemouth bass
fresh-water clams
snag
brown trout
mud & silt
leeches
perch
small mouth bass
loon
lake trout
landlocked salmon
derived from "Water Environments" – The Curious Naturalist – May 1974 – Mass. Audubon.
©1984. E. Parker

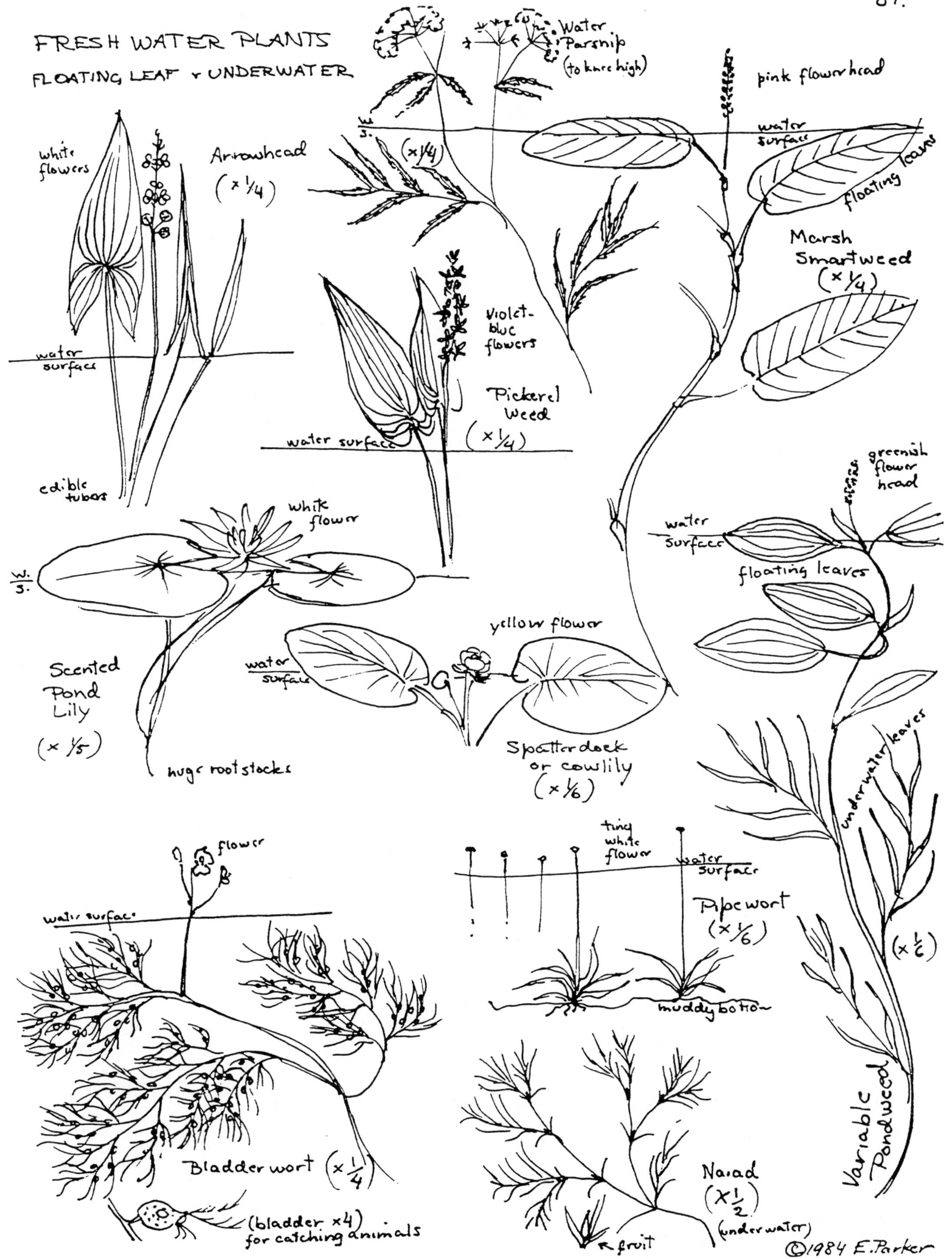
FRESH WATER PLANTS
FLOATING LEAF + UNDERWATER
white flowers
Arrowhead
(x 1/4)
water surface
edible tubers
Water Parsnip
(to knee high)
(x 1/4)
w. s.
violet-blue flowers
Pickerel Weed
(x 1/4)
water surface
pink flower head
water surface
floating leaves
Marsh Smartweed
(x 1/4)
white flower
w. s.
Scented Pond Lily
(x 1/5)
huge rootstocks
yellow flower
water surface
Spatterdock or cowlily
(x 1/6)
greenish flower head
water surface
floating leaves
underwater leaves
Variable Pondweed
(x 1/6)
flower
water surface
Bladderwort (x 1/4)
(bladder x4)
for catching animals
tiny white flower
water surface
Pipewort
(x 1/6)
muddy bottom
Naiad
(x 1/2)
(underwater)
fruit

SLOWER STREAM

(mostly) plants. Mayfly nymphs eat small plants, animals and organic debris. Stonefly nymphs hide on the bottom and eat other animals. These larval forms hatch into flies that are greedily eaten by brook trout as they swarm over the stream. Freshwater smelt may spawn in the sheltered corners, laying eggs that cling to the bottom with adhesive pads. The smelt make their way up small streams from the lakes to lay their eggs. (Saltwater smelt, fished through the ice, run up the rivers to spawn.)

As the stream slows further in flatter terrain©, the bottom becomes muddy and pond like. In the slow river edges and sheltered pond shores, rooted plants float up from the bottom: pondweeds, naiads, marsh smartweed, waterlilies, cowlilies and floating bladderworts. Poking out of the water are arrowheads, pickerelweed, spikerush, waterparsnip, pipewort, sedges, burreed, bulrush and cattails.

(see Purple Loosestrife, p110)

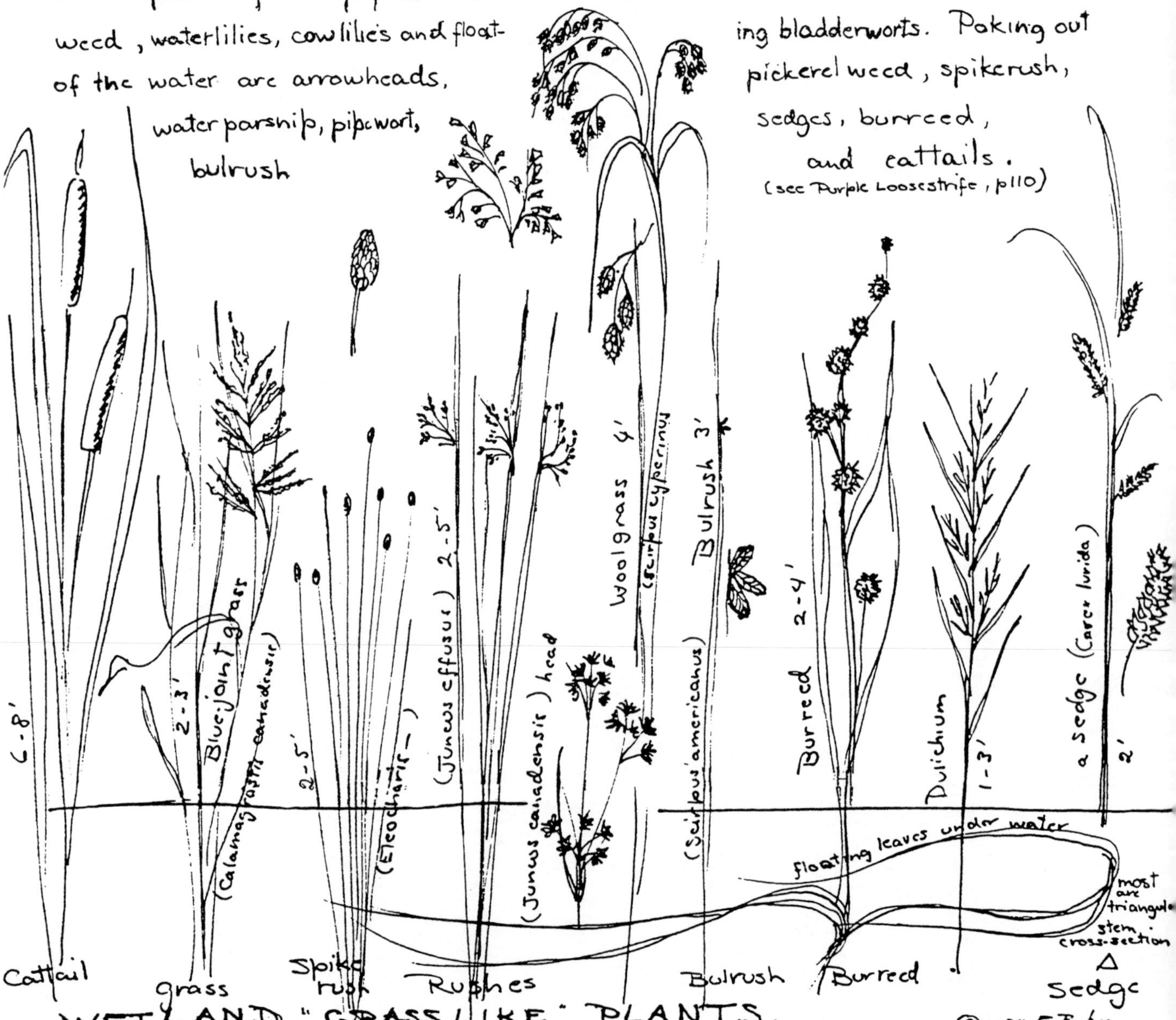

Cattail 6-8'

grass: Bluejoint grass (Calamagrostis canadensis) 2-3'

Spike rush (Eleocharis) 2-5'

Rushes: (Juncus effusus) 2-5'; (Juncus canadensis) head

Woolgrass 4' (Scirpus cyperinus)

Bulrush 3' (Scirpus americanus)

Burreed 2-4'

floating leaves under water

Dulichium 1-3'

Sedge: a sedge (Carex lurida) 2'

most are triangular stem cross-section △

WETLAND "GRASSLIKE" PLANTS.

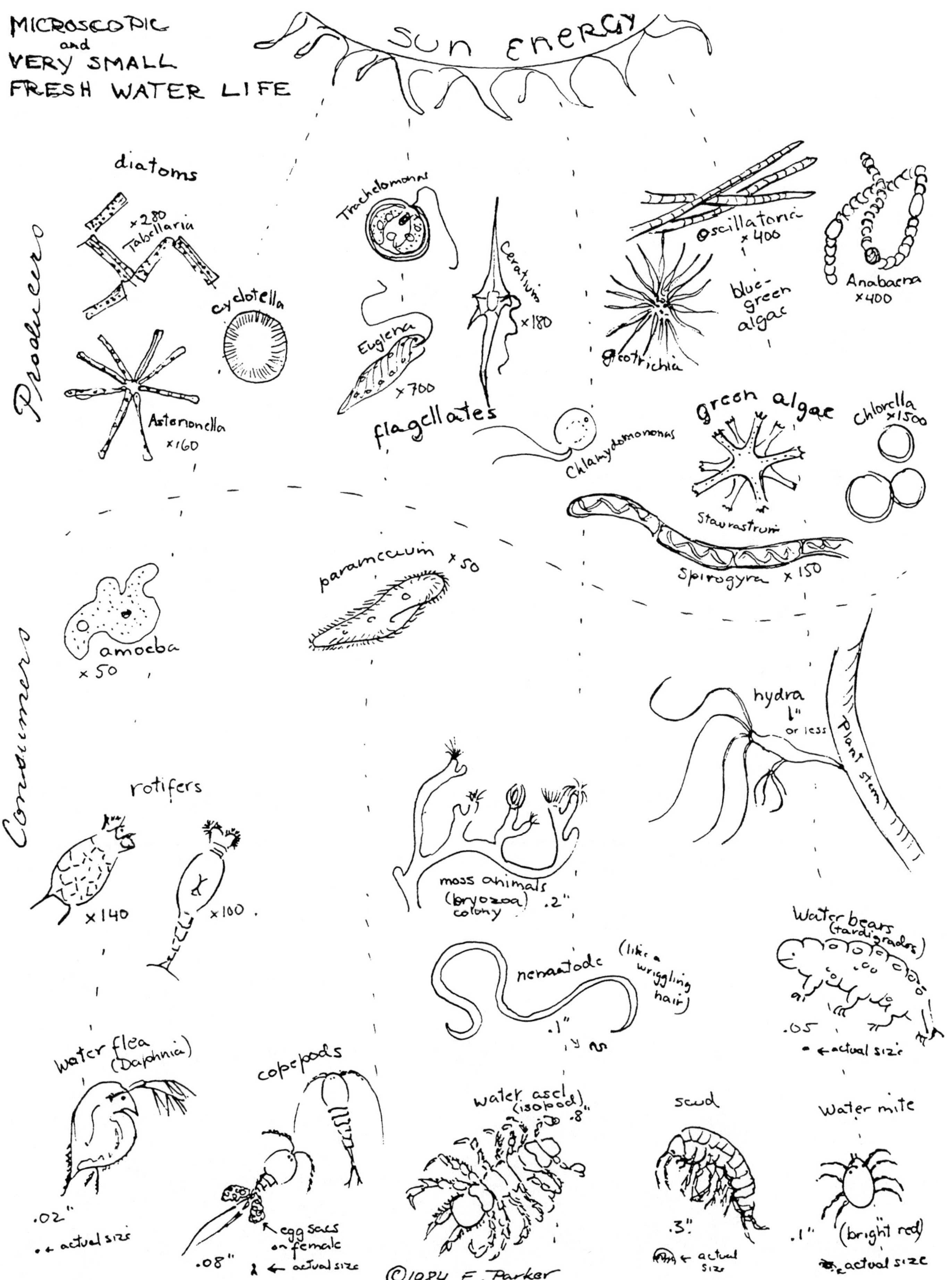
MICROSCOPIC and VERY SMALL FRESH WATER LIFE
SUN ENERGY
Producers
diatoms
x280 Tabellaria
cyclotella
Asterionella x160
Trachelomonas
Euglena x700
Ceratium x180
flagellates
Oscillatoria x400
blue-green algae
Gleotrichia
Anabaena x400
Chlamydomonas
green algae
Staurastrum
Chlorella x1500
Spirogyra x150
Consumers
paramecium x50
amoeba x50
hydra 1" or less
Plant stem
rotifers
x140
x100
moss animals (bryozoa) colony .2"
nematode (like a wriggling hair)
.1"
Water bears (tardigrades)
.05
actual size
water flea (Daphnia)
.02"
actual size
copepods
egg sacs on female
.08"
actual size
water asel (isopod) .8"
scud
.3"
actual size
water mite
.1"
(bright red)
actual size
©1984 E. Parker

ADULT INSECTS

1-2" damsel fly
crane fly 1.5"
caddis fly .5"
dragonfly 2-3
dobsonfly 3-5"
alderfly <1"
mayfly 1.5"
stonefly 1"

SLOW RIVER or POND

The tiny animals swimming about are almost invisible – water fleas (Daphnia), copepods, isopods (water asel), amphipods (shrimplike scuds) and scarlet water mites. Tiny hydra and bryozoa colonies cling to the plant stems. Water bears lie in the mud. They are all eating debris, plant scraps or catching the even smaller protozoans that swim about: Amoeba, Vorticella, Paramecia and flagellates like Euglena. These in turn are eating bacteria and tiny plant cells like diatoms, desmids, green algae like Spirogyra, and blue-green algae like Oscilatoria, Anacbaena and Nostoc. The plant cells are too small to be seen without a microscope, although their bodies may color the water green or form a scum on top during an algae bloom.

The warmer waters teem with creatures. The caddisfly nymphs here have lighter twig cases. Mayfly and damselfly nymphs comb the bottom for food. Big leathery cranefly larvae forage in the muck at the forest edge. Dragonfly nymphs, horsefly and deerfly larvae, big hellgramites (dobsonfly nymphs) stalk the bottoms and stems for animal prey. Giant water bugs grab small fish and tadpoles; backswimmers, with two long oarlike

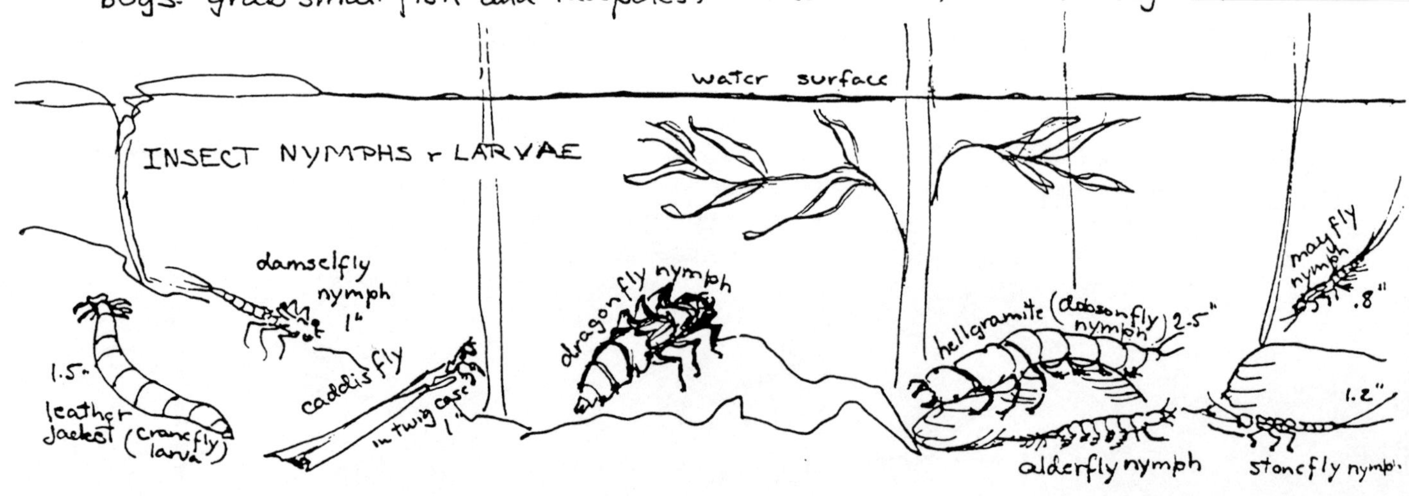

legs catch smaller animals. Water boatmen, with similar paddle legs, eat only algae and debris on the bottom. Little beetles shoot through the water, each carrying a silver bubble of air from which to breathe.

Some creatures use the surface film of the water as their hunting ground (see p. 2). The surface molecules of water cling tightly together ("surface tension") and light insects can stand on top or cling from below. Crowds of shiny black whirligig beetles dart around on still surfaces like carnival bumper cars. Long-legged water striders scoot across the top, each foot resting in a dimple in the water. Mosquito larvae hang under the surface film in still shallow water; they breath through their tails and wave microscopic life into their mouths under water. Some pond snails cling under the surface film, or crawl up and down the plant stems, scraping plant food with their rasp tongues. Along the shallow, muddy shores of the less acid ponds, there are fresh water clams, sifting the water with their siphons ①. Fat leeches hunt for frogs eggs, insect larvae worms and suck the blood of unlucky vertebrates (human beings and others). Leeches can also venture out of the water into damp woods.

In the slowest, most polluted and airless waters (d), only blood worms (larvae of midge flies), mosquito larvae, tubifex worms and the rattailed maggot of the hover fly can live. The "worms" have hemoglobin in their red blood, to better hold the little oxygen there is, and the mosquito larvae and rattailed maggot suck their air from the surface.

The many freshwater insect nymphs eventually crawl out of the water, and emerge from their split skins as mayflies, mosquitoes, blackflies, deerfly, hoverfly, midges, no-see-ums, craneflies, alderflies, stoneflies, dobson flies, delicate damsel flies and the great dragonflies that hawk over the water, hunting for other insects.

Many fish live in the still edge

(d) Life in Polluted water

mosquito
hover fly
phantom midge
mosquito larva
.3"
pupa
tubifex worms
rattail maggot (of hoverfly)
(midge larva) blood worm .2"

LIFE in POLLUTED WATER

① in the dammed part of Megunticook river and lake and in Lake Chickawaukee.

waters, to eat the creatures that breed and feed there. The smallest are minnows, algae and plankton eaters such as golden shiners, and the insect-eating chub. Next in size are the sunfish — bluegills, pumpkin seeds and crappies, and the bigger large-mouth bass of the same family. Bullheads (or hornpout, a brown catfish) feel over the muddy bottom with their long whiskers. Their young swim together in long snaking masses along the shallow edge. White suckers eat small animals and plants with their fat sucking lips. A still pickerel floats in the reedy water, in wait for small fishes or unwary frogs that come by. Brown eels feed on smaller fish, crustaceans and insects. They are born in the Sargasso Sea and come as tiny dark elvers, up the rivers and around the dams, to the quiet fresh waters where they live their adult lives until it is time to go back to the sea to spawn. White perch, smallmouth bass and trout (1) like somewhat cooler waters, deeper and further from shore; brown trout in the warmer lakes, rainbow trout and lake trout (togue) in cooler parts, feeding on insects, crustaceans and smaller fish. The Atlantic salmon used to come up the rivers from the sea to spawn, as did the striped bass, but now only the Ducktrap river in Lincolnville has a fall salmon run (see chart in Inshore-Offshore) They need fish ladders where the dams have been built. Alewives (2) still come up the St. George and Ducktrap rivers, smelt come up the smaller brooks. Megunticook, a deeper, cooler lake, has landlocked salmon, and landlocked alewife. Hosmer Pond, a shallower, muddy lake, and others like it, do not have enough oxygen in their warmer waters for salmon and most of the trout. Fishermen consider most of the shallow warm water fish to be "trash" (3) fish, honoring the trout and salmon as "game" fish.

Many amphibians live in the warm water edge. They lay their eggs in the still waters; great masses of wood frog eggs, strings of toad eggs, round blobs of spotted salamander eggs in clear jelly, can be found

(1) Introduced and stocked from fish hatcheries by Maine Dept. of Inland Fisheries and Wildlife.

(2) Great Brook & Rock brook in the State Park and the brook to the Lily Pond.

(3) Fresh water "trash" fish: sunfish, perch, suckers, eels, chub; Opinions vary over time.

FRESH WATER FISH

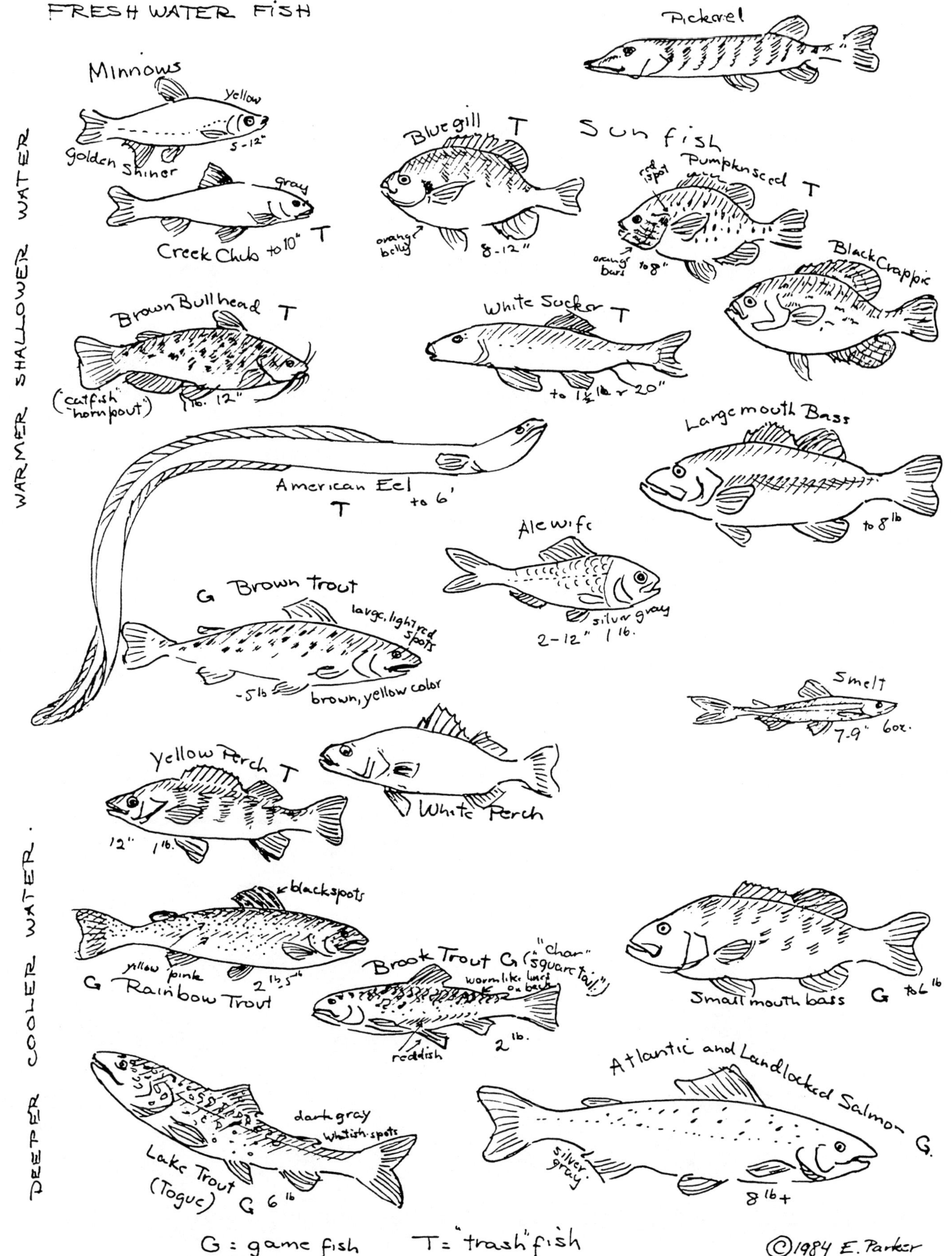

G = game fish T = "trash" fish

FRESH WATER + WETLANDS

Snapping Turtle 10-12"
Loon 24"
Painted Turtle 5-6" in shall
mallards — male, green, female, brown, black, red brown 20-28"
wood duck 13" (quiet swampy ponds)
Green-wing Teal 13-15"
Black duck — actually brown! 21-25"
Blue-wing Teal 15-16
Canada goose 35-40"

AMPHIBIANS

in the spring. They make good food for other pond animals. The frog eggs hatch into the many tadpoles we see in the spring. They eat tiny plants and animals until they lose their gills, grow legs and become frogs. The huge bullfrog tadpoles take two years to do this. Then they eat insects. The spring and summer air is full of the mating song of male frogs and toads: the early spring peepers, the clucking chorus of wood frogs, the twanging of leopard, pickerel and green frogs and the great vibrating bass of the bull frog. Toads have a sweet musical trill. Except for laying eggs, they live away from the water, in gardens and woods, hunting insects + slugs. The salamander and newt eggs hatch into little fish-like larvae with feathery gills and tiny legs. Adult spotted salamander live in the damp woods.

Big snapping turtles live in the ponds and the dammed part of Megunticook River, eating fish, crustaceans and even unwary ducklings. Painted turtles live in the

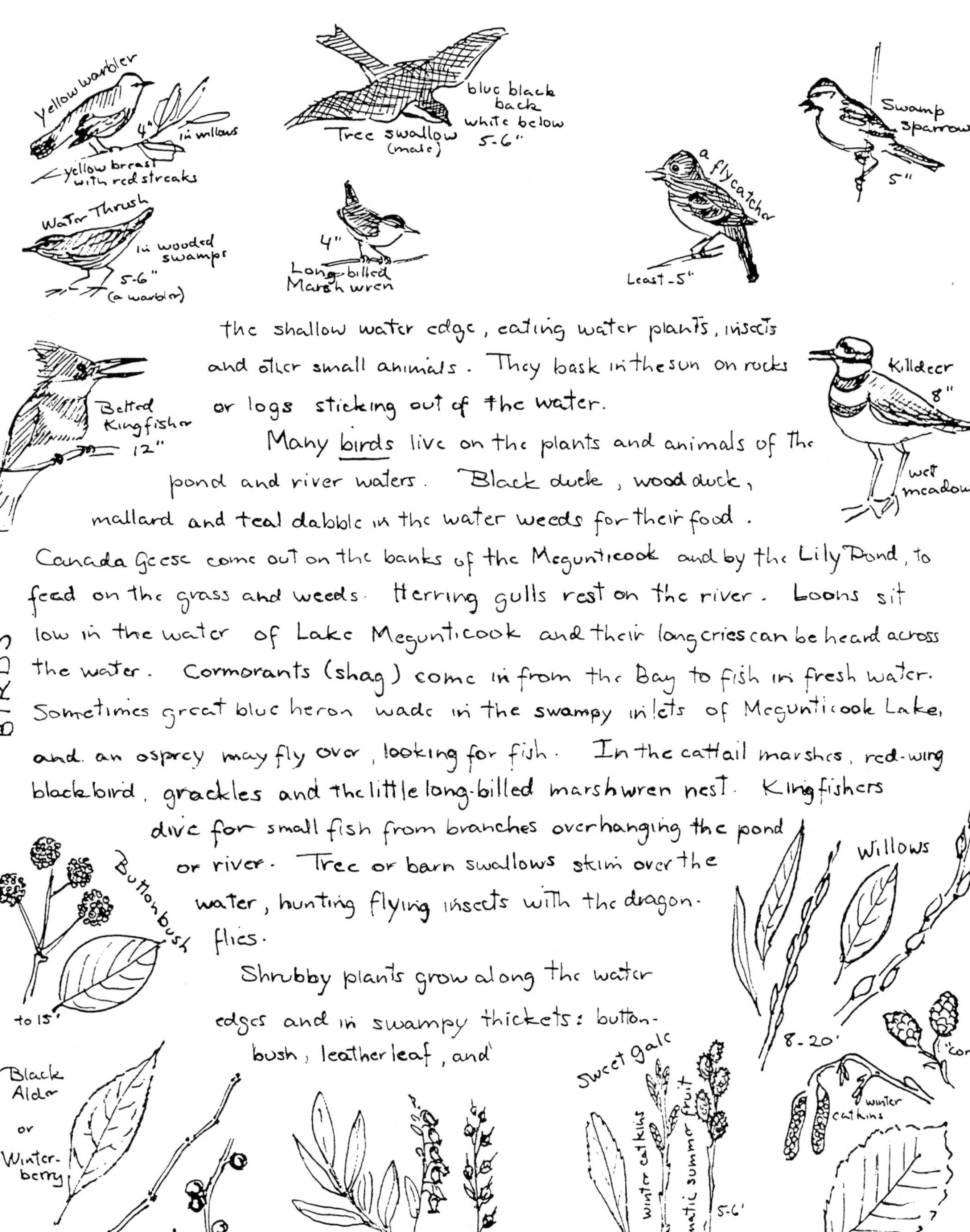

BIRDS

the shallow water edge, eating water plants, insects and other small animals. They bask in the sun on rocks or logs sticking out of the water.

Many birds live on the plants and animals of the pond and river waters. Black duck, wood duck, mallard and teal dabble in the water weeds for their food. Canada Geese come out on the banks of the Megunticook and by the Lily Pond, to feed on the grass and weeds. Herring gulls rest on the river. Loons sit low in the water of Lake Megunticook and their long cries can be heard across the water. Cormorants (shag) come in from the Bay to fish in fresh water. Sometimes great blue heron wade in the swampy inlets of Megunticook Lake, and an osprey may fly over, looking for fish. In the cattail marshes, red-wing blackbird, grackles and the little long-billed marshwren nest. Kingfishers dive for small fish from branches overhanging the pond or river. Tree or barn swallows skim over the water, hunting flying insects with the dragon-flies.

Shrubby plants grow along the water edges and in swampy thickets: button-bush, leather leaf, and

FRESHWATERS + WETLANDS

Little brown bat 3.5"
Meadow jumping mouse 3-4"
Starnosed mole to 5"
Meadow vole 5"
Bog Lemming <4"
water shrew 3-4"

sweetgale, willows and alders, and winterberry ("black alder", a holly). Small birds shelter, nest and hunt insects in these thickets: tiny warblers (yellow throats, water thrush), flycatchers (phoebe, least, alder), veery, sparrows (swamp + song) and goldfinches in the more open places. In the wet meadows, there are bobolinks and nesting kildeer. The killdeer cry out at night sometimes - a long high cry.

MAMMALS

Many mammals visit the wet places for food and some make the edge their home. Water shrews hunt smaller water animals. Little brown bats and other bats hunt flying insects in the warm dusk. Meadow jumping mice, star-nose moles, meadow voles, bog lemmings and big Norway rats all live in the damp edges. Muskrat build island houses of cattails; the cattail is also their favorite food. The beaver often add to the marshlands with their dams, forming ponds that protect them in their large beaver lodges made of sticks and mud. Beaver dams are important in flood control as they slow the runoff in the spring thaw ①. Beavers eat water plants, twigs and inner bark of popple, birches and willow that grow near the water. They store sticks under water for winter eating.

Raccoons like to forage in the wet places, looking for frogs, large insects and small mammals. Mink catch

Muskrat 23"
Muskrat house (made of cattails or rushes or sedges) to 4' long
Beaver 3-4'
In
Pond
beaver lodge of sticks + mud to 10' long
Beaver dam
Norway Rat 12-20"

① Old beaver lodges behind Bog Bridge - some "trial" lodges by young beavers.

Red or Swamp Maple

red stem twigs + buds

red flowers in spring

turns bright red in fall

fish, young birds and mice. The river otter still fishes in some quiet streams. And the great moose wades in the water in the summer (in hidden places), eating water plants, pond weeds, water lilies and sedges. In the spring, they eat the early leaves of alders and willow, wet-land shrubs. ①

Human beings have long been the dominant predator of the wetlands, hunting birds, trapping fur bearers, and catching fish. The swamps and rivers have provided animal and vegetable food for people since the glaciers retreated.

On the wetlands map you will see many patches of forested wetlands. These are only a few of the tiny, boggy places in the forest around us. Depending on the acidity of the soil, these areas may be acid bogs of tamarack and black spruce②, red maple swamps, sweet-soiled cedar swamps of Northern white cedar (arborvitae)② (Beauchamp Point) or willow and alder swales. The alders usually grow in wet parts of fields that have been cleared and allowed to grow back. These plants, much hated by the landowners, are actually nitrogen fixers, holding and enriching the soil as legumes do. The red maple and cedar swamps are carpeted by mossy hummocks, goldthread, clumps of large ferns (cinnamon, ostrich, marsh fern, crested shield fern, oak fern, New York fern – see Forest section). Jack-in-the-Pulpit and great skunk cabbage grow in less acid swamp woods (Beauchamp Pt.) In the understory are highbush blueberry and arrowhead Viburnum. Along the sunny edge: buttercup, forget-me-not and touch-me-nots② Many

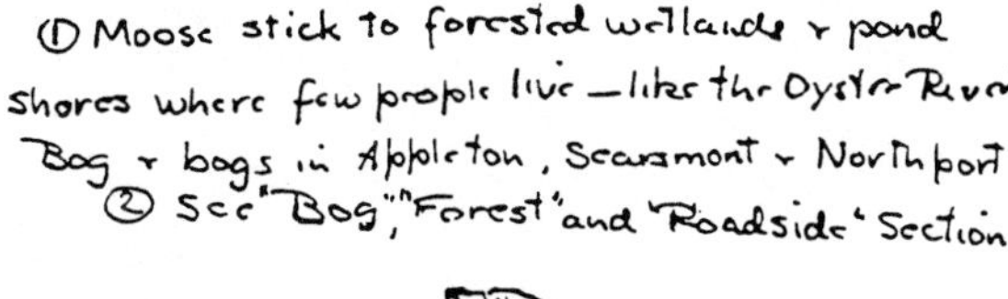
① Moose stick to forested wetlands + pond shores where few people live – like the Oyster River Bog + bogs in Appleton, Searsmont + Northport
② See "Bog", "Forest" and "Roadside" Sections.

FRESHWATERS + WETLANDS

insect-catching birds, warblers and flycatchers, etc., live in the rich wet woods.

Freshwater wetlands, rivers and ponds are very susceptible to environmental damage. Things are always draining into wet places. Eroded soil washes in from earthmoving projects, road building, house building, plowed fields and logged hillsides where the forest has been carelessly cut and the plant cover destroyed by heavy vehicles. The silt fills rivers and ponds and suffocates the water animals by clogging their gills. We have a fair amount of new construction in the area; earth is left bare during storms and silt runnoff is a common occurrence.

The construction of beaches and landing places along pond shores can harm habitats of the shore creatures ① Fresh concrete and creosoted wood in piers poison the surrounding water. The least harmful structures are removable floats and floating docks. The plants and animals are relatively undisturbed.

The small dams were built on our rivers to provide water power for mills, but they also changed the nature of the river upstream, making small ponds where there had been fast running water. The populations of plants and animals changed accordingly and the spawning fish runs ② declined and largely disappeared, with resulting drops in salt water fish catches of river-spawning fish.

Pesticides used on crops, forests and roadside brush are carried into the streams where they poison plant and animal life. In our general area, apple orchards, blueberry fields and roadsides are regularly sprayed.

Sometimes, too many nutrients (nitrogen and phosphates), are washed into ponds from septic tanks

fluffy white flowers

Boneset

2'

Purple Loosestrife

2-4'

① eg. the sand at Shirttail spreads over the bottom and not much can live there.

② alewife, salmon, smelt striped bass

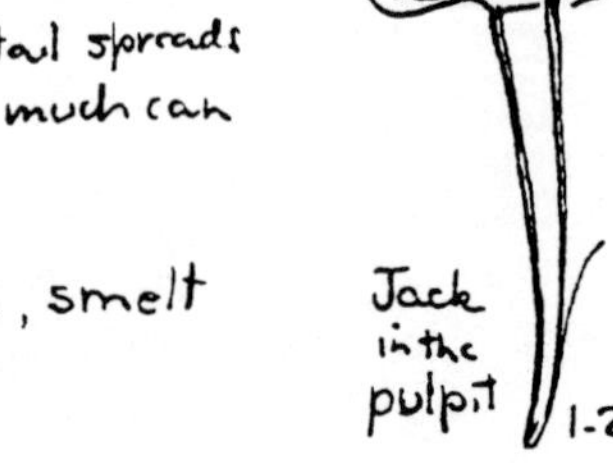

that leak, leach fields that are overloaded and raw sewage from lake-side cottages. Fertilizer on fields and manure heaps can leach into ponds. This can cause algal "bloom" on the water. A bright green spring bloom is caused by abundant algae and usually does no harm. But the late summer blooms, caused by blue-green algae like Anabaena, can form a smelly wind-blown scum, and the bacteria that decompose the algae after they die can use up so much of the water's oxygen that the animal life suffocates. This occurred several years ago on Nortons Pond in Lincolnville and it can happen in small ponds near chicken houses.(1)

Landfills and dumps can leach toxic wastes into surrounding wetlands and streams. This is a worry we still have. Our old dump is drained by a sluggish red stream which goes to the Lily Pond. The limestone quarry-hole beneath the dump is water-filled and likely to leach into the surrounding ground water. Any solvents, motor oil, paints and household cleaners that we threw out are likely to get into the water system of the land around.

Acid rain, which comes from acid air pollution(2) could make our lakes too acid for fish to live, as has happened in the Adirondacks of upper New York state.

We need to pay attention to these hazards and try to moderate our construction and waste-disposal habits, so that our wetlands, ponds and rivers will continue to be the rich living places they are.

Great blue heron 38"

(1) a golden "bloom" seen in the spring on the water of Lake Megunticook is only pine pollen.

(2) mostly SO_2 from sulfurous fuel (used in industrial cities of the MidWest) and NO_2 from automobile exhaust (local) - see FOREST section.

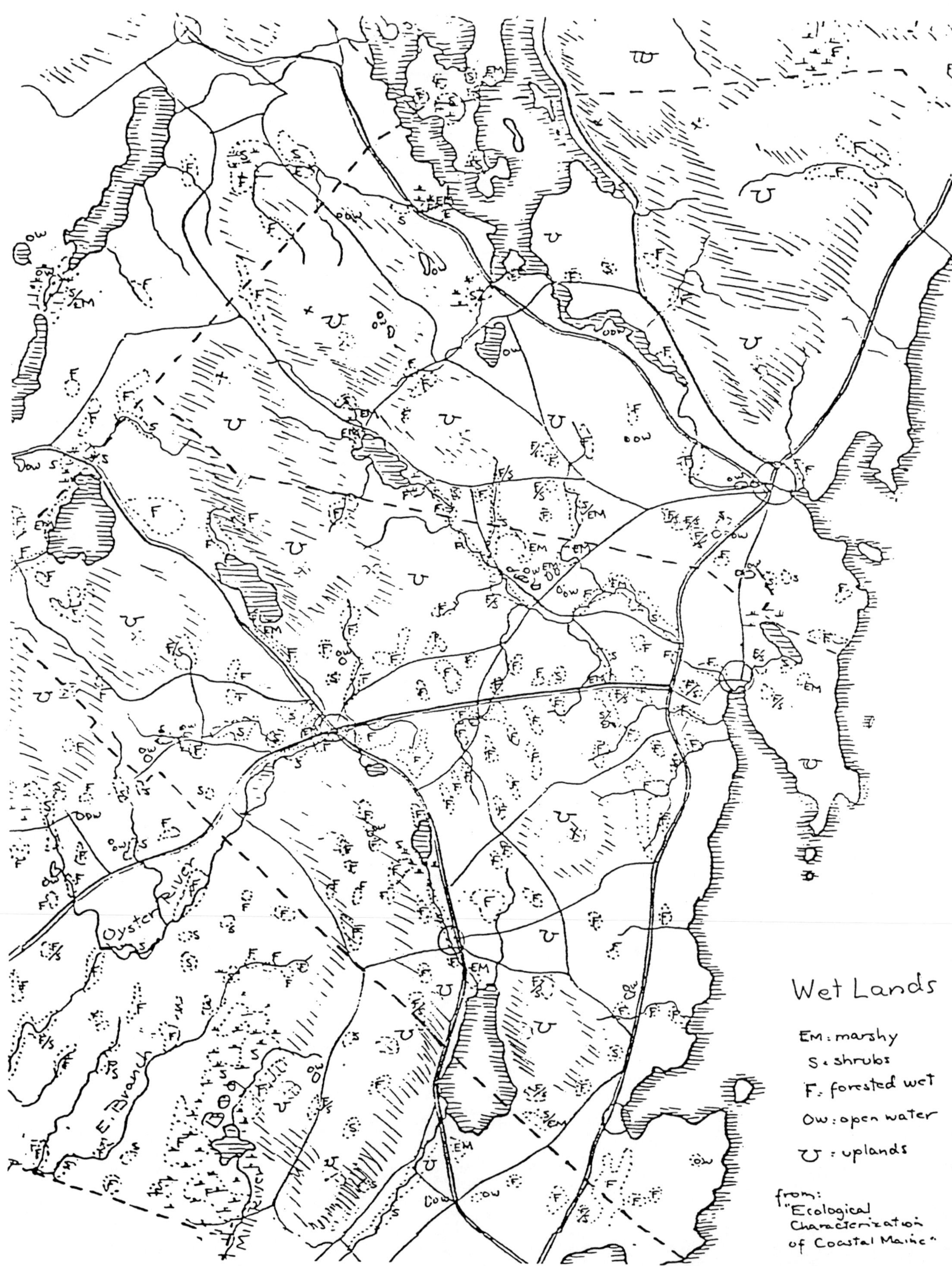
Wet Lands
EM: marshy
S: shrubs
F: forested wet
Ow: open water
U: uplands
from:
"Ecological
Characterization
of Coastal Maine"
Oyster River
E. Branch

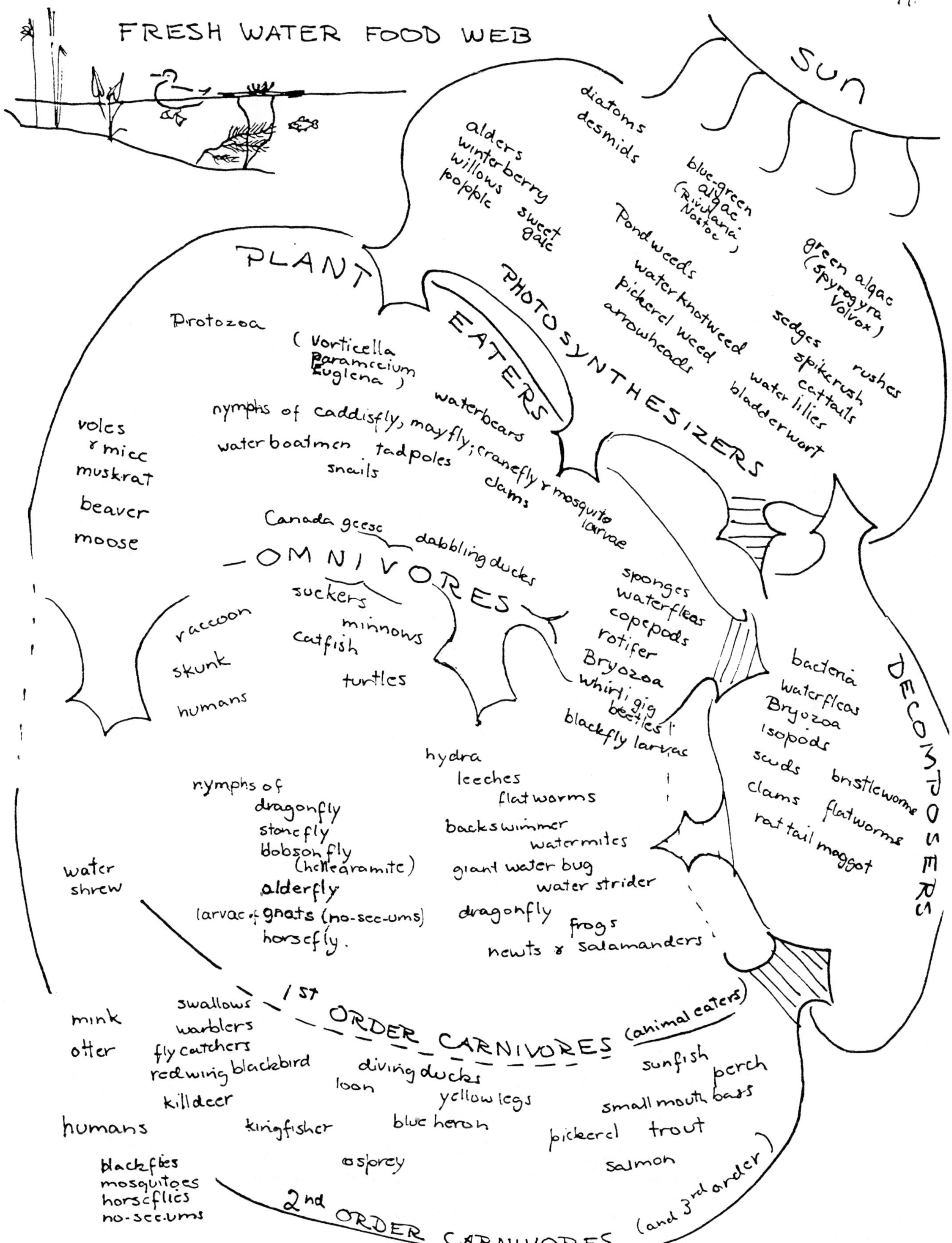
FRESH WATER FOOD WEB
SUN
PHOTOSYNTHESIZERS
diatoms
desmids
blue-green algae (Rivularia, Nostoc)
alders
winterberry
willows
popple
sweet gale
Pondweeds
water knotweed
pickerel weed
arrowheads
green algae (Spyrogyra, Volvox)
sedges
rushes
spikerush
cattails
water lilies
bladderwort
PLANT EATERS
Protozoa
(Vorticella
Paramecium
Euglena)
waterbears
nymphs of caddisfly, mayfly; cranefly & mosquito larvae
water boatmen
tadpoles
snails
clams
voles & mice
muskrat
beaver
moose
Canada geese
dabbling ducks
OMNIVORES
suckers
minnows
catfish
turtles
raccoon
skunk
humans
sponges
waterfleas
copepods
rotifer
Bryozoa
whirligig beetles
blackfly larvae
DECOMPOSERS
bacteria
waterfleas
Bryozoa
isopods
scuds
bristleworms
clams
flatworms
rat tail maggot
hydra
leeches
flatworms
nymphs of
dragonfly
stonefly
dobson fly
(hellgramite)
alderfly
larvae of gnats (no-see-ums)
horsefly.
backswimmer
watermites
giant water bug
water strider
dragonfly
frogs
newts & salamanders
water shrew
1st ORDER CARNIVORES (animal eaters)
mink
otter
swallows
warblers
fly catchers
redwing blackbird
killdeer
humans
kingfisher
diving ducks
loon
yellow legs
blue heron
osprey
sunfish
perch
small mouth bass
pickerel
trout
salmon
blackflies
mosquitoes
horseflies
no-see-ums
2nd ORDER CARNIVORES (and 3rd order)

BOG

The shape of our land was left as it is by the last retreating glacier. The great weight of the advancing ice scoured the mountains smooth with grinding

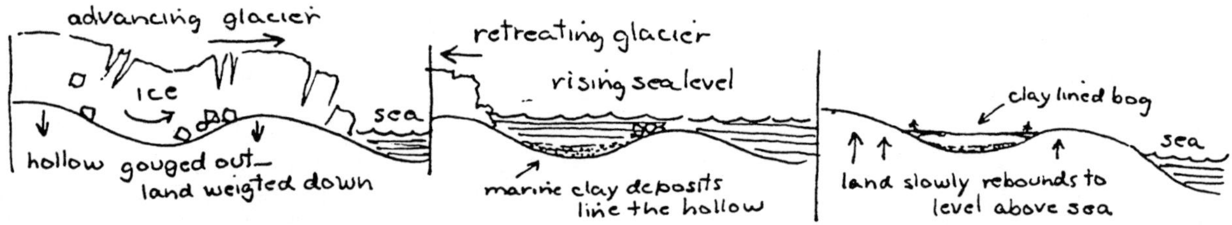

rocks and gouged out hollows in the land. As the glaciers retreated, the melting ice dumped barriers of gravel that blocked the drainage of the hills. The seas rose with water from the melting ice and impermeable clays were deposited in the depressions. As the land gradually rose again, released from the weight of the glacier, these undrained hollows were left full of water that doesn't move. Some of these lakes and ponds became bogs.

In motionless water, the oxygen is quickly used up by living organisms and is not replenished as in moving waters. Without oxygen, bacteria cannot break down the bodies of the plants that colonize the water-filled depression ①. The water becomes more and more acid because of the accumulated organic acids of the undigested plant material ②. High acidity of the water makes it difficult

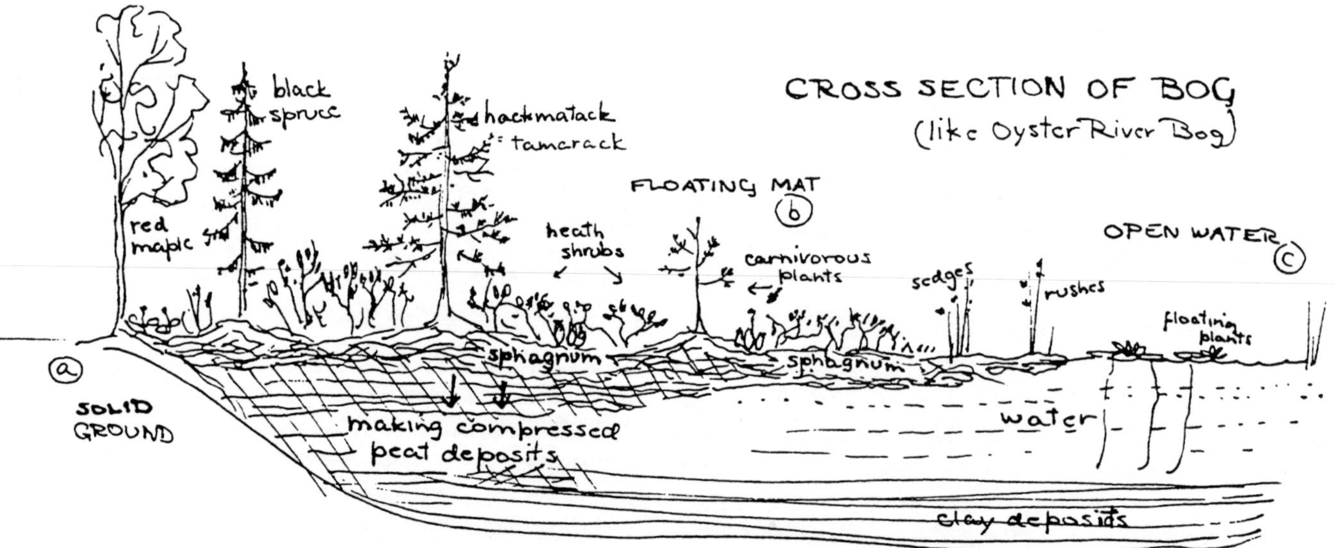

① The bodies of animals are not broken down well either in a peat bog, which is why the bodies of the bog people of Denmark have been dug up in perfect condition.

② Bog pH is ≈4, whereas pure neutral water preferred by most living things is pH 7 (or slightly acid, 6.5)

for plants to absorb minerals. At this point, only plants that can survive these acid conditions remain.

Sphagnum is a moss which lives and grows under these conditions. These moss plants have large water-storage chamber cells and can absorb water like a sponge. The sphagnum plants make a springy water-logged mat over the surface of the bog, partly floating on the water. The dead material falls off the bottom of the mat and accumulates in thick layers of peat on the bottom. Eventually the whole bog is filled with compressed, undecomposed plant bodies: peat which can be used in gardening or cut into bricks, dried and burned as a fuel.(3)

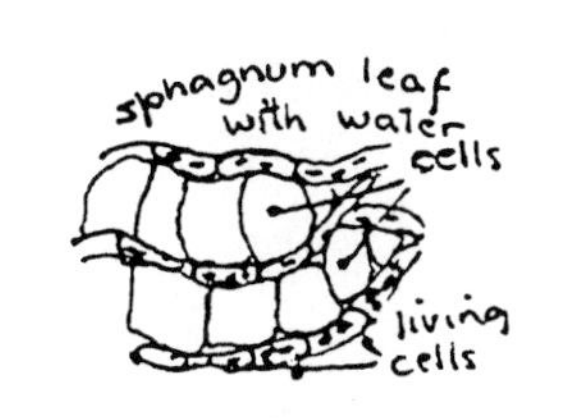

The sphagnum also keeps the bog water and air cool, by holding water and allowing it to evaporate, like a great airconditioner. The other plants that live on the sphagnum mat tend to be northern, acid-tolerant species. Many are of the heath family (like blueberries) and very similar in appearance: Labrador tea, leatherleaf, bog rosemary, rhodora, lambkill ... They are all low shrubs with small leathery leaves. These plants are living in water but they can't use it because it's too acid, so they have the kind of leaves that preserve the fresh rain water they get.

A few common bog plants have a special way of getting the minerals they need but cannot absorb from the acid water. They resort to catching and digesting insects to obtain the nitrogen and other nutrients they need. The tiny sundew plants have sticky globules on the tips of the hairs on their leaves. These shine in the sun and attract insects which are then stuck fast. The hairs bend inwards and the blade of the leaf folds around the victim which is then absorbed. The pitcher plant attracts flies to its pink sugared "lip". The fly slides down the slippery inner wall and is digested by an enzyme in the liquid inside the "pitcher". Another animal-eating plant, the bladderwort, lies floating in bog pools. It has threads hanging below the surface of the water. On these threads are small bladders, 1/10th of an inch wide,

(3) Peat is used in Ireland, Scotland and other countries in northern Europe, as fuel.

Bog Plants

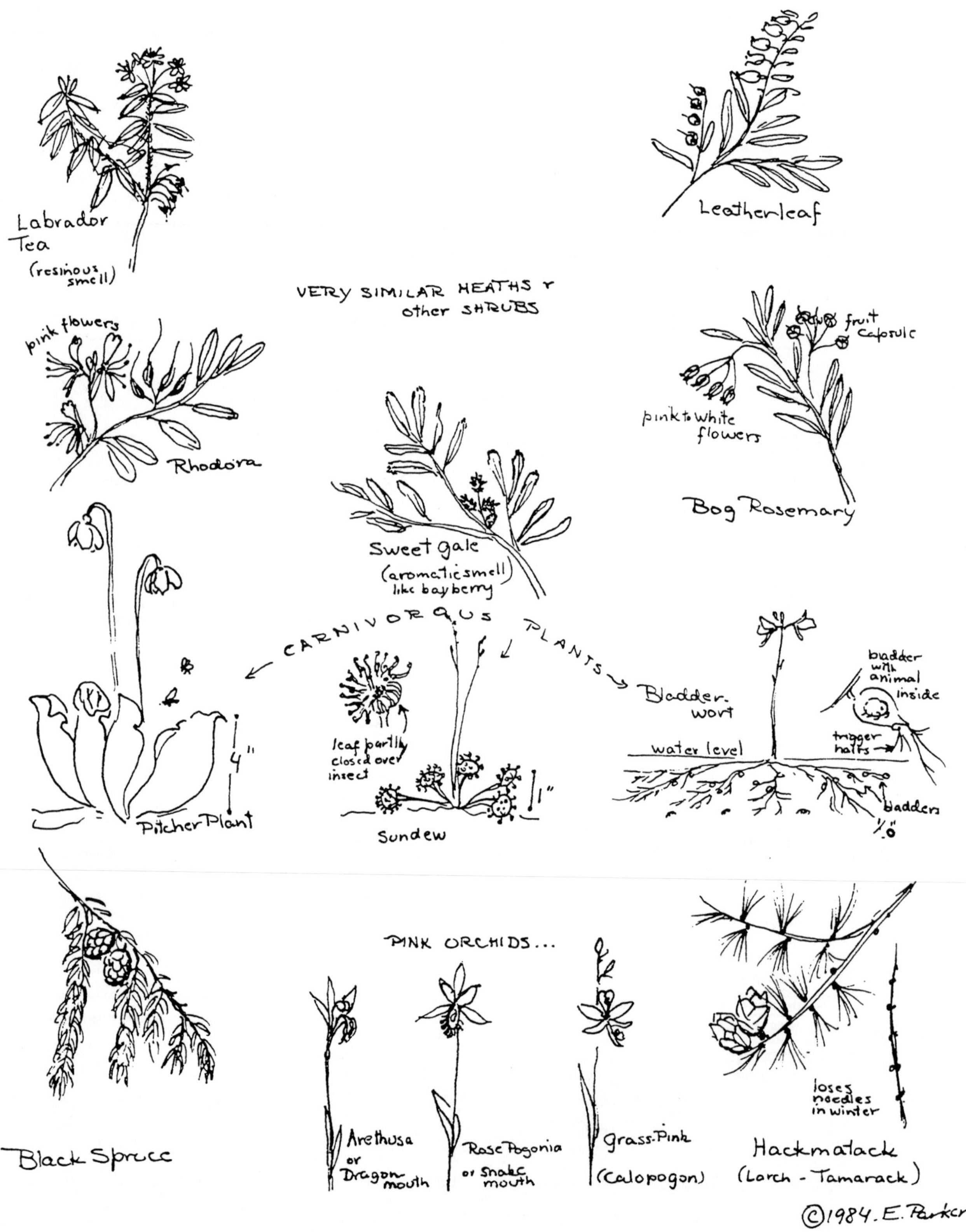
Labrador
Tea
(resinous smell)
Leatherleaf
VERY SIMILAR HEATHS &
other SHRUBS
pink flowers
Rhodora
fruit capsule
pink to white flowers
Bog Rosemary
Sweet gale
(aromatic smell)
like bayberry
CARNIVOROUS PLANTS
leaf partly closed over insect
4"
Pitcher Plant
1"
Sundew
Bladder-wort
water level
bladder with animal inside
trigger hairs
bladders
1/8"
PINK ORCHIDS...
Black Spruce
Arethusa
or
Dragon mouth
Rose Pogonia
or Snake mouth
Grass-Pink
(Calopogon)
loses needles in winter
Hackmatack
(Larch - Tamarack)

which open suddenly when microscopic animals swim by, sucking them in.

The bog is arranged in an orderly fashion. Around the border,(a) on more solid land, are red maple, red spruce, white pine, white birch and red oak. On the forest floor beneath are mosses and ferns, especially big cinnamon ferns, and the same spring flowering plants that live in other Maine forests. The black spruce, more tolerant of the cool acid soil, edges into the wet bog. The boldest trees are the hackmatacks (larch, tamarack), on island hummocks and peninsulas made by their roots, out on the sphagnum mat.

The next zone is that of the heath shrubs and other shrubs, shallow-rooted on the compressed sphagnum. Fragrant sweet gale (a relative of bayberry) and Labrador tea give off an incense smell as you brush through the thicket. There are pink masses of blooming rhodora in the spring, and patches of white tufted cotton grass that blows in the wind. Underfoot are creeping cranberry stems and tiny sundews. You might see colorful orchids blooming in the early summer: Arethusa ("dragon mouth"), rose pogonia, and grass-pink. As you venture closer to open water, the ground becomes springier. You are now on a mat floating over water. Stand on a firm grassy hummock and bounce, gently, with arms outstretched. The hackmatack on the next hummock will bounce too, as your motion is transmitted across the mat.

In the center of the younger bog(c) is open water[4]. It looks like a real pond, with rushes and waterlilies, frogs and dragonflies.

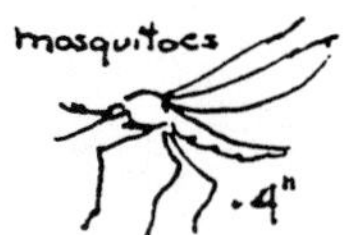

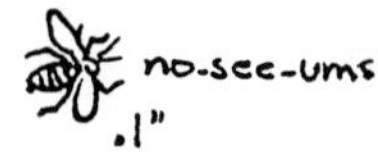

In the spring, the bog and the woods around it are full of flying insects: mosquitoes, blackflies and no-see-ums. You venture in to see the flowers and hear

[4] This is true of the Oyster River or Rockland Bog, because of the work of the bog's beavers.

the birds at your peril. The blackflies cluster on dark clothing, attracted as to the dark pelt of a moose or bear. The woods are also full of warblers that have come north to nest and feed on the insects. Each kind of bird has its characteristic "song" with which the male claims and holds its territory. The air rings with their challenging cries.

The streams leading out of the bog are frequented by beaver. Their works raise the water level in the bog. Moose visit the edge of the bog in season; they are especially adapted to make their way through the water-laden ground. Their wide splayed feet keep them from breaking through the matted surface into the mire below. The moose are like the bog plants, creatures of a more northern climate, that still live in this cool damp place left by the glaciers.

For a more detailed list of animals living near the bog, see the mammal habitat chart.

The Oyster River Bog Association, with members from Rockport, Rockland, Thomaston and Warren who own property in the Bog and its surrounding woods, are working together to preserve the Bog and its special plants and animals.

LAND MAMMAL HABITATS

from "Ecological Characterization of Coastal Maine"
● preferred
○ acceptable

	In or near lakes, ponds rivers, streams	Marshes, bogs wetlands	Meadows	Shrubs - old field	Edge of field & forest	Deciduous forest	Mixed forest	Coniferous forest	Rural	Urban
beaver	●	●				○				
(black bear)	○	○				○	●	○		
bobcat			○	○	●	●	●	●	○	
bog lemming (southern)		●	○			○	○	○	○	
(coyote)		○		●	●	●				
deer mouse					○	●	?	●	○	
eastern chipmunk				○	●	●	○		○	○
fisher					○	○	●	○		
	○			●	●					
grey squirrel				○	●	●	○		○	○
house mouse			○						●	●
little brown bat	●		●			○	○	○	●	○
longtail weasel	○			●	●	○				
(marten)							○	●		
meadow jumping mouse	●	●	●	●						
meadow vole	○	○	○	○	○	○			○	
mink	●	●				○	○	○		
moose	●	●			○	○	○	○		
muskrat	●	●								
northern flying squirrel							●	●		
norway rat	○	○							●	●
* porcupine						○	●	○		
pygmy shrew	○					●	●	●		
racoon	●	●			○	●	●		○	○
red fox			●	●	●	●	●			
red back vole							○	●		
red squirrel					○	○	○	●	○	
short tail shrew	●		●	●	●	●	○	●		
snowshoe hare				●	●	●	●	●		
starnose mole	○	●	●							
striped skunk			●	●	●				○	
water shrew	●					●	●	●		
white foot mouse				●	●	○	○			
whitetail deer	○	○		●	●	○	○	○		
woodchuck	○		●	●	●	○			○	
woodland jumping mouse	●					●	●	●		
* otter	●	●								

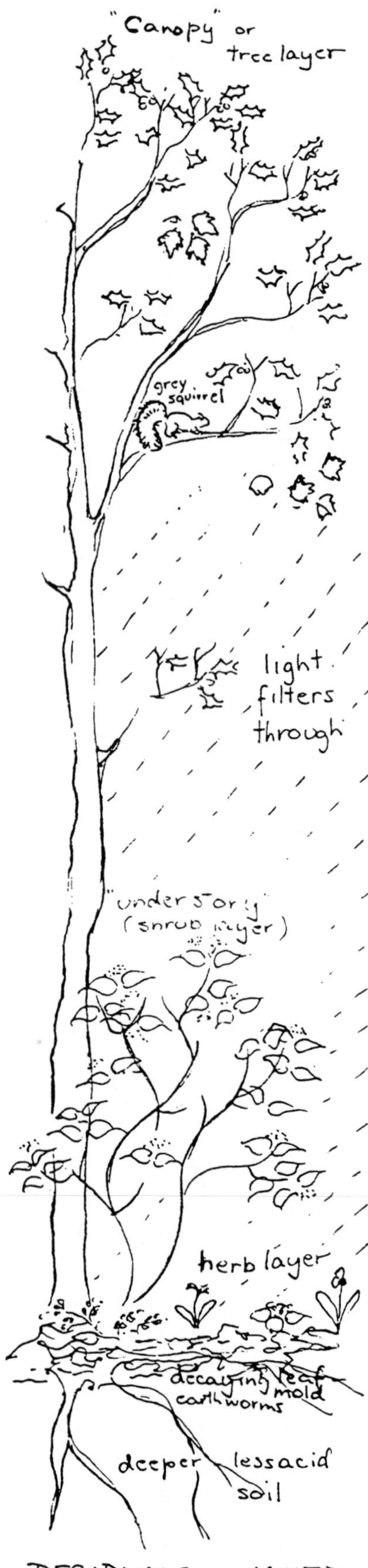

DECIDUOUS and MIXED FOREST

FOREST

The land around us is covered by forest. Trees grow over the mountains, along lakes and streams, down to the edge of the sea. Everywhere that there is enough soil that is not covered by water, there are trees growing. People have cut them back to make fields in places, but they grow back in time unless the soil is washed away or the land is paved over.(1) This forest grows in our region because there is enough soil and rain fall to support trees which then shade out other sun loving plants, like grasses. The plants that live under the trees must make do with what sun they get.

Our woods may be deciduous (of trees with broad leaves that fall in the autumn), coniferous (evergreen, cone bearing) or mixed. The plants and animals that live in their shelter vary accordingly. The deciduous forest may be thought of as being organized in horizontal layers. Highest is the "canopy" or tree layer, receiving most of the sun in the summer. These are the maples, ash, birches and oak(2). Below the canopy is the "under story" or shrub layer, catching the light that filters through the leaves above. Here are witchhazel, striped maple and mountain maple, the viburnums (witherod, nannyberry, highbush cranberry, mapleleaf viburnum, hobblebush), alternate-leaved dogwood, elderberry, honeysuckle, raspberry, black-

(1) see "Roadside and Field" section for description of how the forest grows back after a field is abandonned.

(2) Our beeches seem to be mostly small, having been infected by a beech scale disease which killed many larger beeches, 20 to 30 years ago. In Rockport, there is a grove of healthy American Chestnut trees, remnants of the great trees that lived before the chestnut tree blight spread through the East Coast of the U.S. (early 1900's).

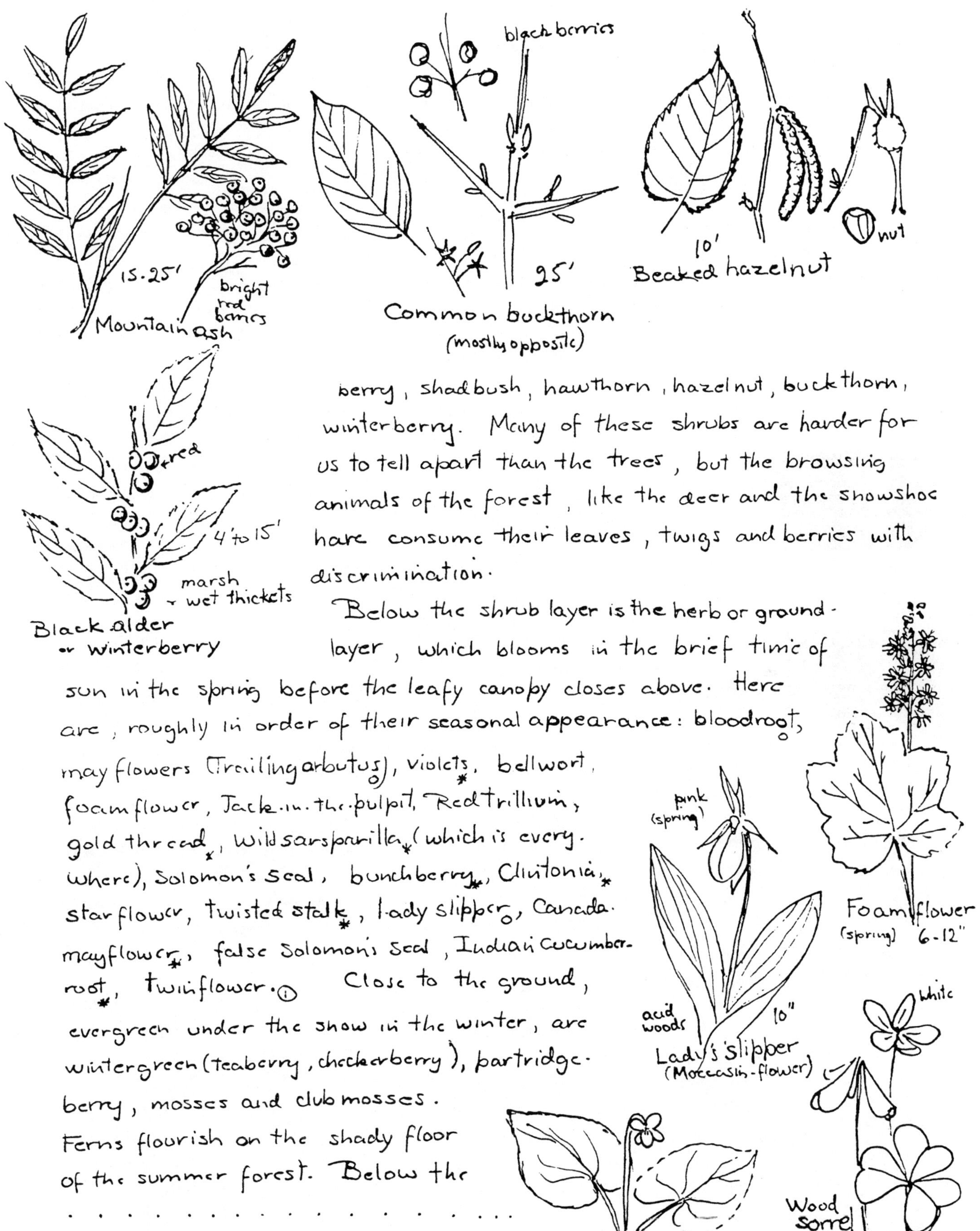

berry, shadbush, hawthorn, hazelnut, buckthorn, winterberry. Many of these shrubs are harder for us to tell apart than the trees, but the browsing animals of the forest, like the deer and the snowshoe hare consume their leaves, twigs and berries with discrimination.

Below the shrub layer is the herb or ground-layer, which blooms in the brief time of sun in the spring before the leafy canopy closes above. Here are, roughly in order of their seasonal appearance: bloodroot°, mayflowers (Trailing arbutus°), violets*, bellwort, foamflower, Jack-in-the-pulpit, Red trillium, gold thread*, wild sarsparilla* (which is everywhere), Solomon's seal, bunchberry*, Clintonia*, starflower, twisted stalk*, lady slipper°, Canada mayflower*, false Solomon's seal, Indian cucumber-root*, twinflower.(1) Close to the ground, evergreen under the snow in the winter, are wintergreen (teaberry, checkerberry), partridge-berry, mosses and club mosses.

Ferns flourish on the shady floor of the summer forest. Below the

. . . .

(1) common flowers are starred *
rare flowers = o

DECIDUOUS TREES (leaves not to scale)

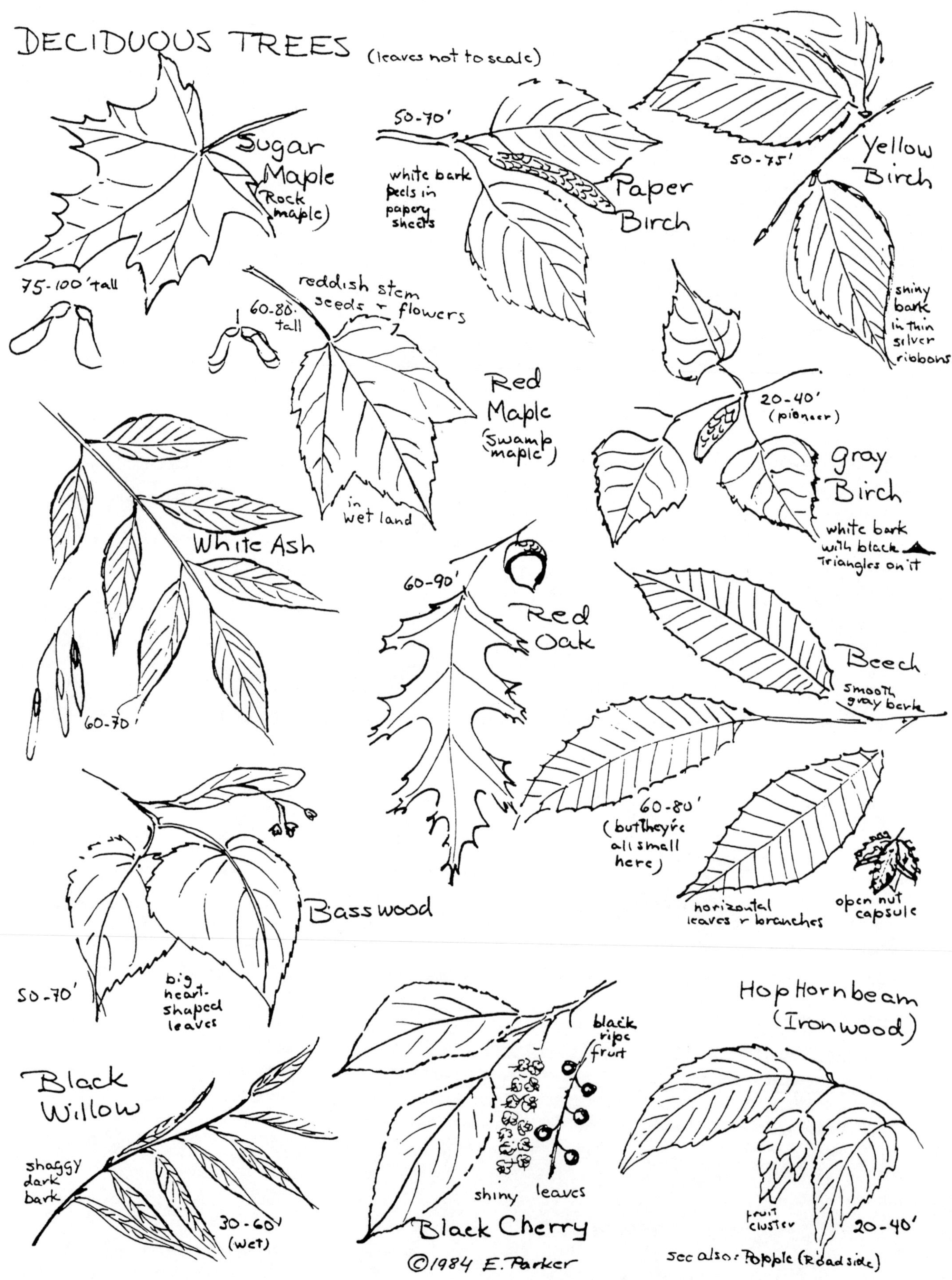

FOREST

ground in the layer of leaf mold and inside the moldering trunks of dead trees is an active world of soil makers.(1)

The main food of the forest are the trees themselves: their leaves, seeds, sap, bark and wood. As the air and earth warm in the spring, the insect life that sleeps in the ground and in the trees, wakes, moves, changes and begins to eat. Flies and moths hatch out of pupating grubs and hasten to lay their eggs in fertile places. Overwintering egg masses become masses of caterpillars that chew the leaves of the forest: cankerworms (inch worms), sawfly larvae, sprucebudworm, forest tent-caterpillars. Aphids and leaf hoppers suck sap from the leaves and young stems. Most insects specialize in particular plants. As the insects emerge with the warming trend, many birds arrive from the south to eat them: vireos thrushes, many kinds of warblers (living in particular habitats) swallows, wrens, flycatchers. The air is filled with the sound of buzzing insects and the songs of birds competing for nesting territories. The forest is consumed in a frenzy of activity. Under the bark & wood of sick and dead trees, bark beetles, wood borer grubs are tunneling and eating. Woodpeckers drill into the punky wood of dead limbs to extract the grubs and beetles. Graceful ichneumon flies carefully deposit eggs in borer grubs with their long delicate ovipositors. Wasps carry off caterpillar pieces for their own young to eat after hatching. In the evening,

(1) See SOIL food web. in GEOLOGY section.

Little brown bat 3½"

Hornets & yellow jackets .8" eat caterpillars, etc.

Ichneumon Fly 1.4" ovipositer laying eggs in horntail larva

INSECT EATERS

Wood thrush 7" (brown) bell-like call

Ovenbird "teacher" call 5½" on forest floor one of the many warblers

.05" Aphid Leaf-hopper (sapsucking)

Canker worm, Inchworm 1" eat leaves

Sawfly .1" eat leaves 1.5"

Spruce Bud Worm 1"

Forest tent caterpillar 1.5"

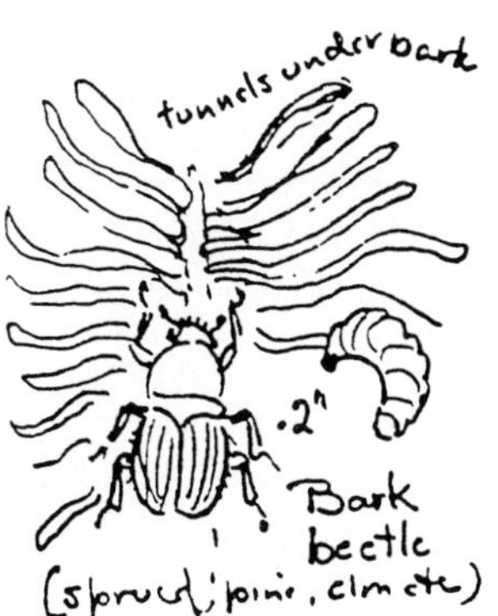

does the boring 1" Borer some are "Long-horned beetle" diff. kind eat dead wood, poplar, sugar maple

TREE-EATING INSECTS

SHRUBS & SMALL TREES - DECIDUOUS FOREST 22
(understory)

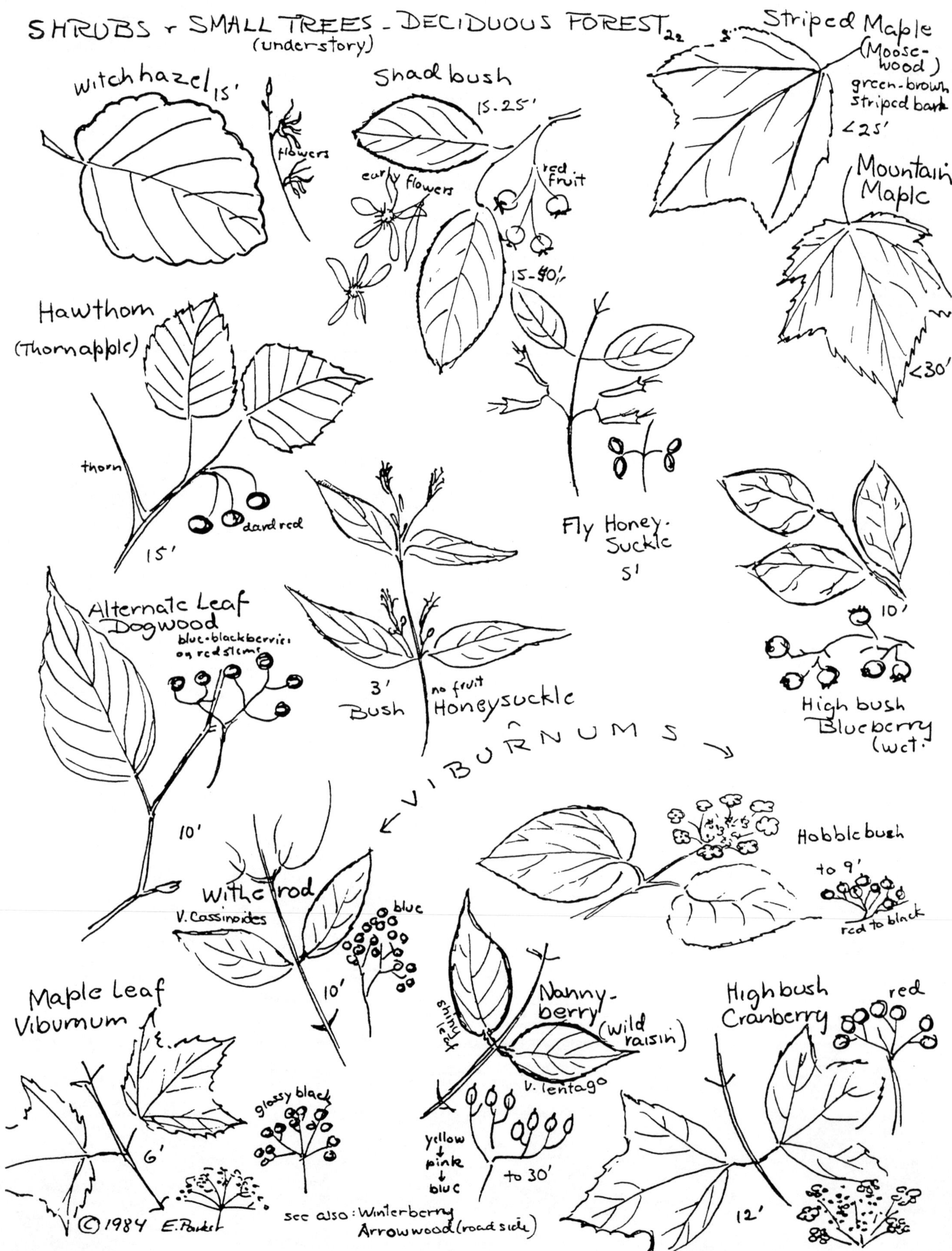

see also: Winterberry
Arrowwood (road side)

FOREST

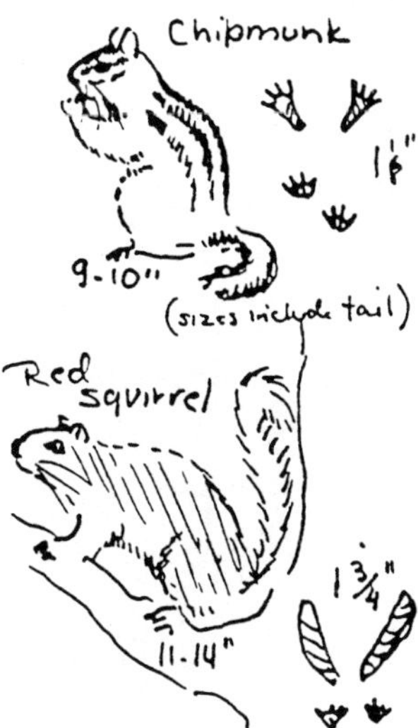

bats come out to hunt the flying insects. A few amphibians and reptiles live on the forest floor, living largely on insects and worms: redefts (newts), salamander, tree frogs. DeKay snakes.

Other animals also eat the trees and the plants under them. The lumbering porcupine eats inner bark of the trees, perching incongruously on a branch against the trunk. The smaller rodents; chipmunk, woodland jumping mouse, white footed mouse, boreal red-backed vole, red squirrel (coniferous trees) and gray squirrel (deciduous trees) all eat seeds, nuts, berries and occasional insects. The ruffed grouse finds seeds and berries near the ground.

All these animals, and the browsing deer and snowshoe hare, find more food close to the edge of the forest where more light enters and there are more shrubs with berries, buds and leaves to eat. For this reason, we have more deer in Maine now that people have cut clearings. Before the settlers came there were relatively fewer deer and more moose, who eat the popple and birch and alder leaves, and water plants along the edges of streams, lakes and bogs.

shrew 4"
(eats insects)

The plant eaters are in turn eaten by weasels, including the fisher (who prefers porcupine), red fox, racoon, and skunk.

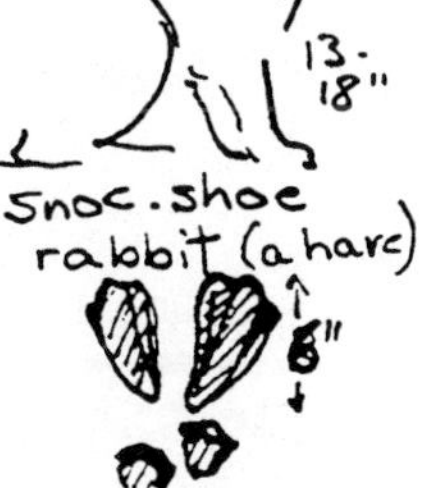

FOREST FLOOR - SPRING FLOWERS

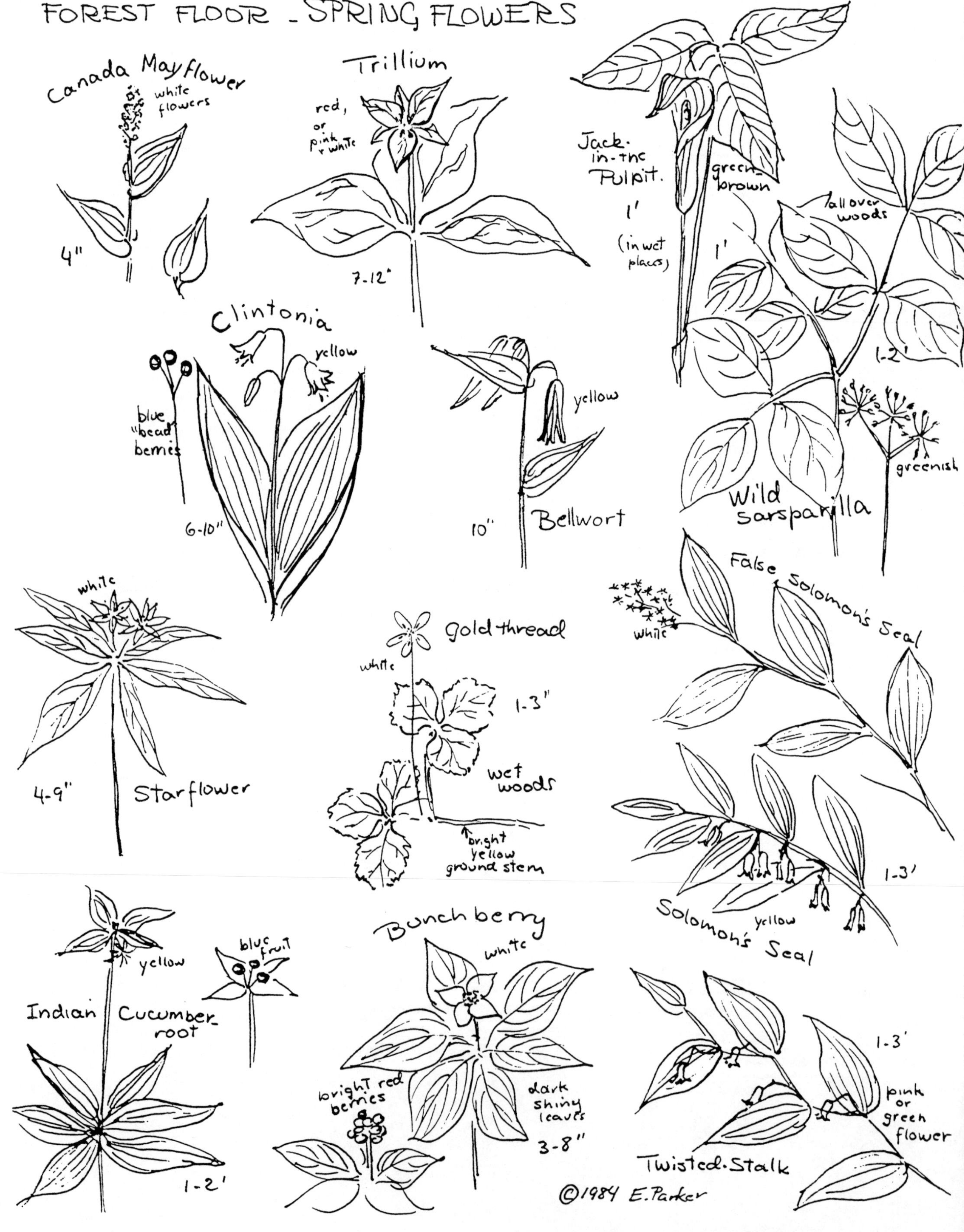

FOREST CALENDAR

blooming dates can vary as much as a month - according to weather

	1st week	2nd week	3rd week	4th week
MARCH	sap running	chickadee call		swelling popple & willow buds
APRIL		catkins on popple & willow; skunk cabbage →; ↓ first green shoots on forest floor →	red maple bloom →; bloodroot; ← mayflower →; spring peepers sing at night in wet places	sugar maple bloom
MAY	fiddleheads →; white violets; blue violets; trout lily; E. phoebe	first tiny leaves on trees (SUN IN FOREST); Shad bloom; red trillium; BLACKFLIES →; wood thrush; ← bluets →; hobblebush & other viburnums; vireo; warblers arriving	canada mayflower; chokecherry; strawberry flower; wild sarsparilla; foamflower; red berried elder; red baneberry flower; mourning cloak butterfly	Pink lady's slipper →; Jack-in-the-pulpit; painted trillium; ← bellwort →; false solomon's seal; big ferns out; early meadow rue; apple blossom; black cherry
JUNE	rhodora (bog edge); ← buttercups →; forget-me-nots; bunchberry; twisted stalk; starflower; indian cucumber; ← clintonia; columbine →	FOREST LEAVES PROVIDE HEAVY SHADE; ← gold thread →; partridgeberry; raspberry bloom; spring blue (tiny butterflies)	wood betony; blackberry bloom →	tall meadow rue
JULY	pyrola →; shinleaf →; ← twinflower →; deer flies →; wood sorrel	pipsissewa; blueberries in clearings; wintergreen; raspberries	shinleaf	← indian pipe → (↑ ↓); turtlehead
AUG	blackberries →; cicadas start →; ← mushrooms (↑ ↓)	← jewelweed →; ← nuthatch calls → (↑); after rains →	BERRIES: viburnum; dogwoods; bunchberries; whorled wood aster; white wood aster; noisy jay families	beechdrops; white lettuce (rattlesnake root)
SEPT.	heart leaf aster →; ← gall-of-the-earth →		warblers leave	LEAVES START TURNING; FIRST FROSTS; few insects
OCT.		animal coats thicken	witchhazel bloom →	
NOV.	LEAVES ALL DOWN (except a few oak & beech leaves); WIND & RAIN →		↓	
REST of the WINTER	TRACKS in SNOW: snowshoe hare - grey squirrel	fox - bobcat (skunk & raccoon on warm days)	crows; chickadees; woodpeckers...	snow fleas, on snow, warm days.

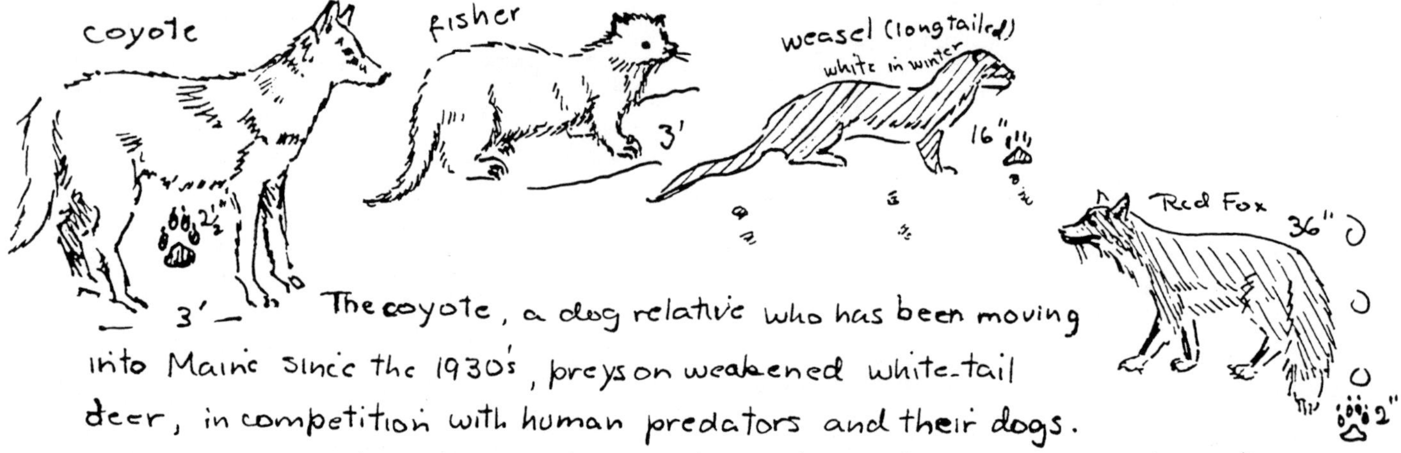

The coyote, a dog relative who has been moving into Maine since the 1930's, preys on weakened white-tail deer, in competition with human predators and their dogs. The black bear that once lived here has retreated to more remote northern forests and hills as the population has grown, though there have been signs of bear recently. Our hawks, broadwing, red-tailed & redshouldered, that normally prey on rodents and songbirds have almost disappeared, probably because human use of pesticides has disturbed their ability to reproduce.

When the leaves of the trees and the remains of animals fall to the forest floor, they are returned to the soil by the labor of bacteria, and fungi, fly and beetle larvae. The soil of the deciduous and mixed forest is rich and well aerated, containing earth worms and other animals that plow and redistribute the decomposed organic and mineral material needed by the plants of the forest. The roots of the trees reach deep below the humus layer to bring up dissolved minerals of the parent rock material below. Carbon and nitrogen from plant and animal remains are drawn out of the humus layer. The cycle begins again with the re-building of plant material in the tree canopy.

2⅝"

skunk. <20"

In the winter, the forest becomes very quiet. Most of the birds leave as the insect life subsides in the autumn, from cold and lack of food. Only the seed eaters, the scavengers and the woodpeckers remain. Grouse peck over dried berries and seed heads. Grosbeaks, crossbills and finches break open seed capsules. Black capped chickadees find seed and dormant insects. The wood-peckers, nuthatches and tiny brown

raccoon <30"

4¼"

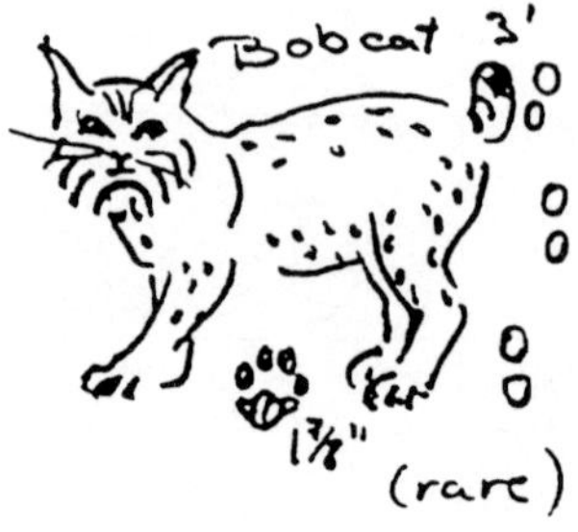

FOREST

great horned owl
18"

Downy woodpecker
7"

White breasted nuthatch
5"
creeps down
(blue gray)

Brown creeper
5"
spirals up

creepers study the tree bark for overwintering larvae and pupae. Crows and jays scavenge everything animal and vegetable. The great horned owl watches for rodents; But we have few owls; they have gone, like the hawks. Some years we have an "invasion" of snowy owls from Canada, during especially cold winters.

The leaves fall as the light fails, so that the plants will not dry out in the cold, dry winter winds. Some animals retreat into shelters to sleep. (bats, chipmunk, jumping mice). The tracks of snowshoe hare, white-foot mouse, fox cross the fresh snow.

In years of deep snow, the deer yard up under sheltering evergreens where they trample the snow down and use short trails to reach the evergreen boughs and deciduous buds which they eat during the winter. They cannot manage deep snow with their slender legs and sharp hooves

Most of our forest on the Camden Hills is "mixed", but in some places there are dense stands of conifers, usually spruce, but sometimes pine in dry places, or cedar in wetter places. The conifers can resist drying winter winds with their tough, waxy needles. They catch sunlight earlier and later in the year than the deciduous trees. The forest floor below them is dark and covered with a dense layer of needles. There is no shrub layer, although young balsam fir may grow here and there in small stands, never reaching a great height. There is very

FOREST

little ground cover: some clumps of moss, lichens on fallen trees, some ferns. The dense coniferous forest is a much more limited environment than the deciduous forest. The acid soil and the acid tree needles inhibit the action of soil bacteria and earthworms; most of the breaking down is done more slowly by a network of fungi mycelia under the ground. The mycelia send up spore-bearing mushrooms after rains. The roots of the trees are shallow and use symbiotic fungi (mycorrhiza) to absorb soil nutrients. The soil is typically poor and leached by rainfall. Fewer animals live in this habitat than in the deciduous forest: larva (like the spruce budworm), wood boring beetles, wood ants, wood wasps, red squirrels and crossbills who can extract seeds from cones. The evergreen forest feels quiet, dark and empty in comparison with the busy deciduous forest.

The coniferous forests were an earlier stage of vegetation over our land. These trees could live on the early soils left by the glaciers. They could stand the cold winds, poor drainage and acid soils. Before them were the earlier soil builders, the lichens and then the mosses

FOREST BIRDS

Jan Feb Mar Apr. May June July Aug Sept. Oct. Nov. Dec.

SUMMER BIRDS

(hawks) warblers E. phoebe veery R.C. kinglet wood thrush vireo brown thrasher

veery wood thrush brown thrasher E. phoebe vireo R.C. kinglet warblers (hawks)

YEAR ROUND: Hairy & Downy woodpecker, Great Horned Owl, Blue Jay, Crow, Blackcapped chickadee, Nuthatches, Brown creeper, Grosbeaks, Crossbills, Ruffed grouse.

WINTER BIRDS (snowy owl) rough legged hawk, pine siskin, red poll, pine grosbeak

WINTER BIRDS

red squirrel

dense shade

few species of plants and animals

mosses

ferns

mushrooms

shallow tree roots

layer of undecayed needles

network of fungus mycelia

poor, shallow, leached acid soil on porous rock or gravel foundation

CONIFEROUS FOREST

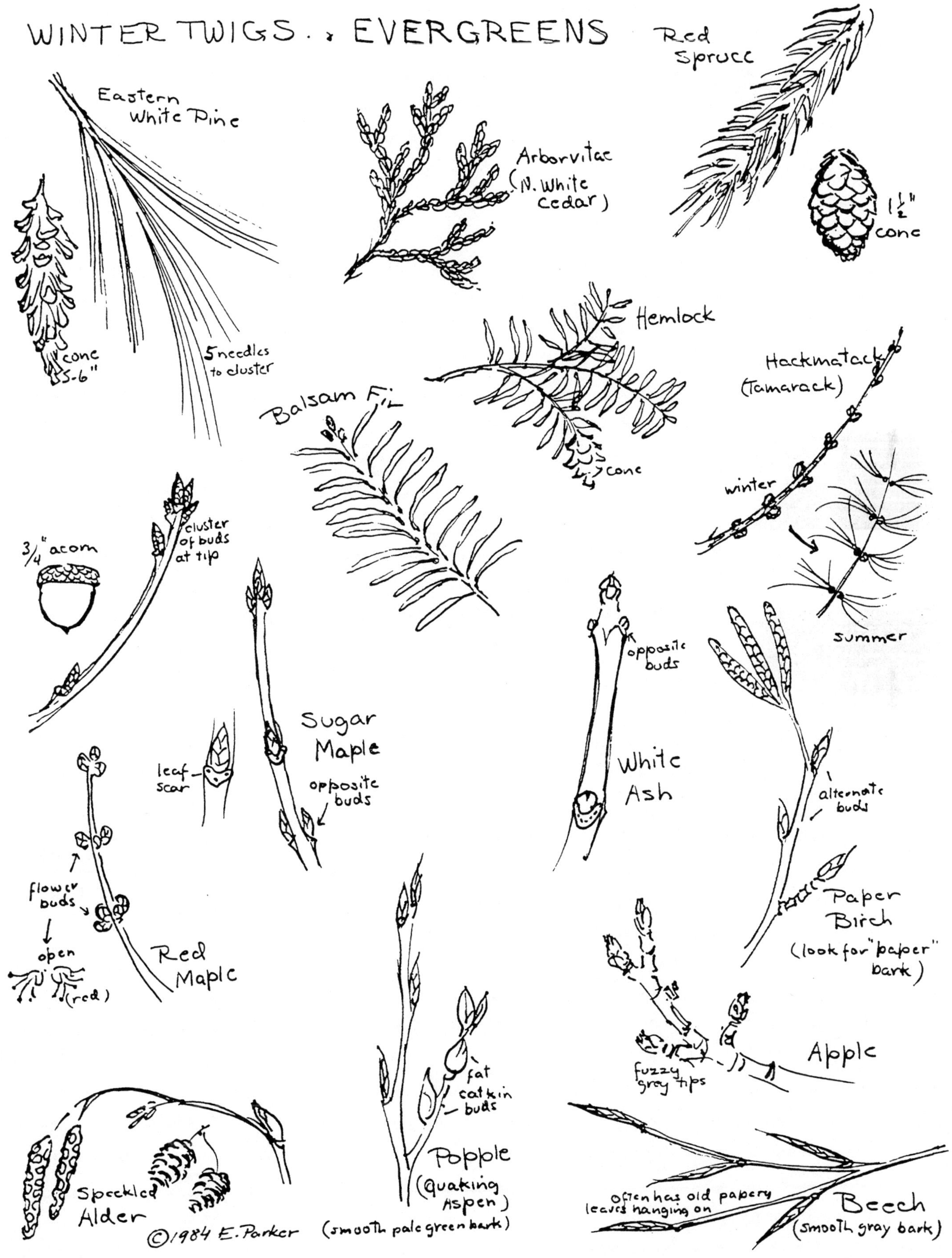
WINTER TWIGS . EVERGREENS
Red Spruce
1½" cone
Eastern White Pine
cone 5-6"
5 needles to cluster
Arborvitae (N. White cedar)
Hemlock
cone
Hackmatack (Tamarack)
winter
summer
Balsam Fir
3/4" acorn
cluster of buds at tip
Sugar Maple
leaf scar
opposite buds
White Ash
opposite buds
alternate buds
Paper Birch (look for "paper" bark)
flower buds
open
(red)
Red Maple
Apple
fuzzy gray tips
fat catkin buds
Popple (Quaking Aspen)
(smooth pale green bark)
Speckled Alder
often has old papery leaves hanging on
Beech (smooth gray bark)

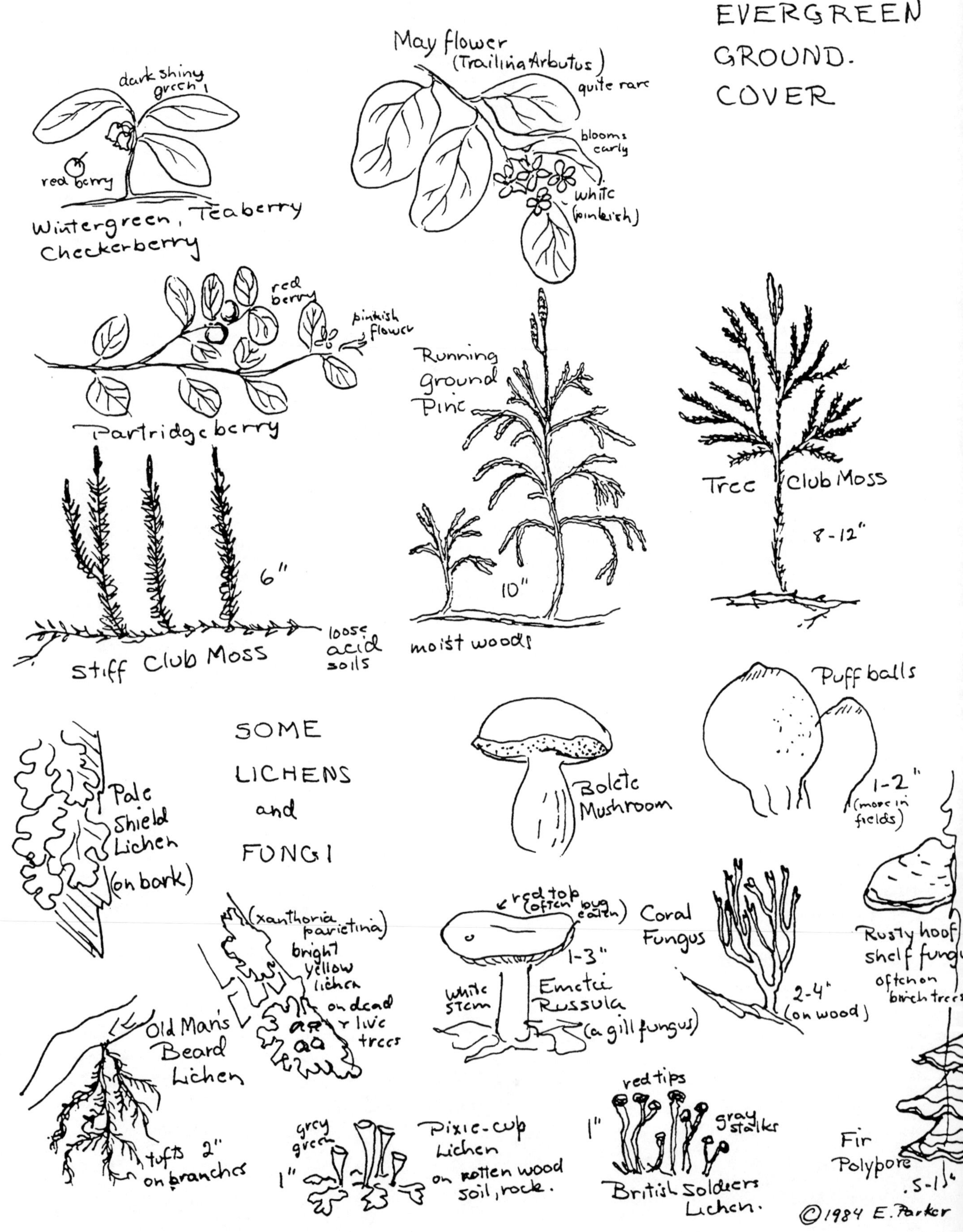
EVERGREEN
GROUND.
COVER
dark shiny green
red berry
Wintergreen, Teaberry
Checkerberry
May flower
(Trailing Arbutus)
quite rare
blooms early
white (pinkish)
red berry
pinkish flower
Partridgeberry
Running ground Pine
10"
moist woods
Tree Club Moss
8-12"
6"
Stiff Club Moss
loose acid soils
SOME
LICHENS
and
FUNGI
Pale Shield Lichen (on bark)
Bolete Mushroom
Puff balls
1-2" (more in fields)
(xanthoria parietina)
bright yellow lichen
on dead & live trees
red top (often bug eaten)
1-3"
white stem
Emetic Russula
(a gill fungus)
Coral Fungus
2-4" (on wood)
Rusty hoof shelf fungu
often on birch trees
Old Man's Beard Lichen
tufts 2" on branches
grey green
1"
Pixie-cup Lichen
on rotten wood soil, rock.
red tips
1"
gray stalks
British Soldiers Lichen.
Fir Polypore
.5-1"
©1984 E. Parker

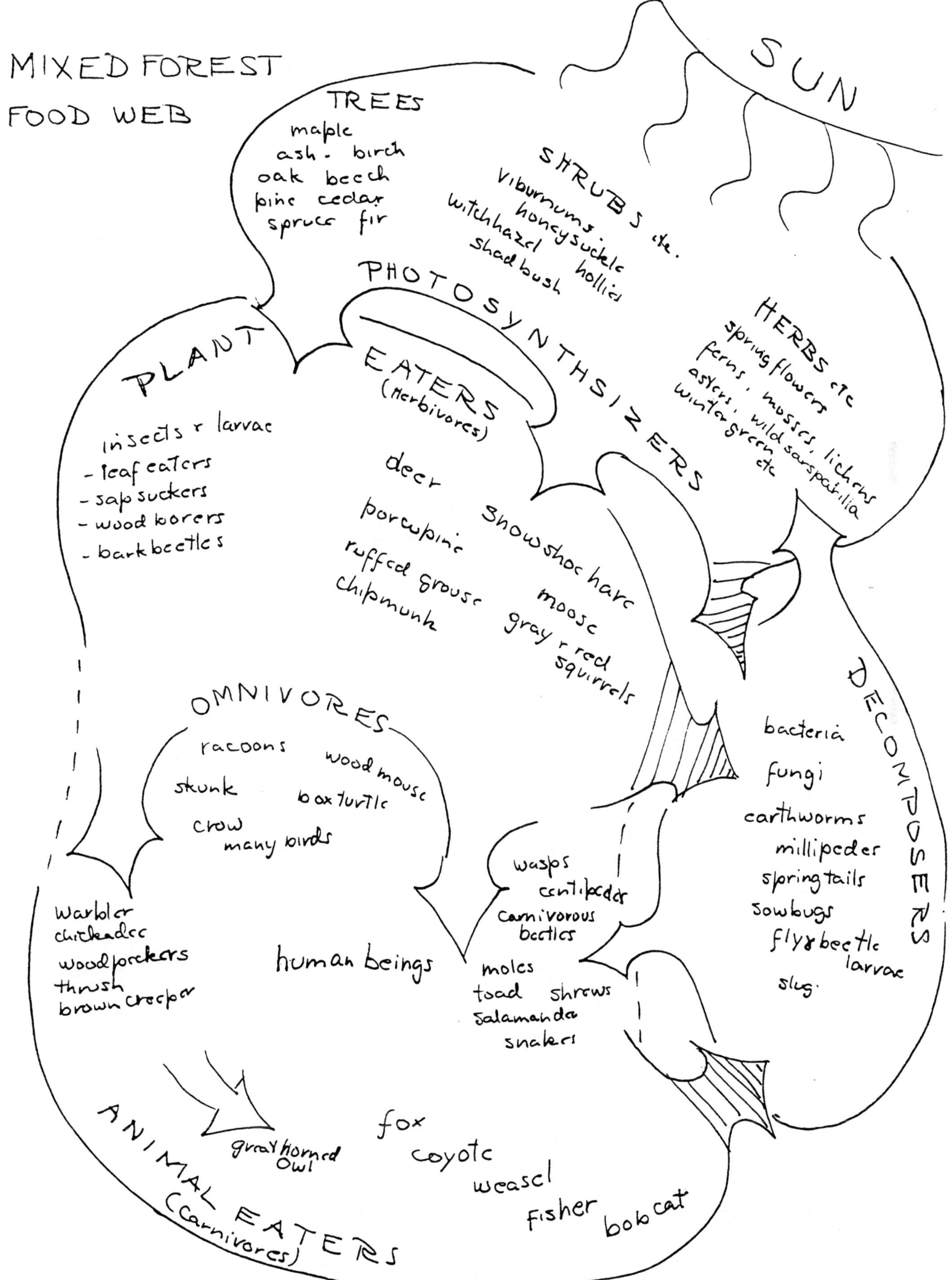
MIXED FOREST
FOOD WEB
SUN
TREES
maple
ash - birch
oak beech
pine cedar
spruce fir
SHRUBS etc.
viburnums.
honeysuckle
witchhazel hollies
shadbush
PHOTOSYNTHSIZERS
HERBS etc
spring flowers
ferns, mosses, lichens
asters, wild sarsparilia
wintergreen
etc
PLANT EATERS
(Herbivores)
insects & larvae
- leaf eaters
- sap suckers
- wood borers
- bark beetles
deer
porcupine
snowshoe hare
ruffed grouse
chipmunk
moose
gray & red
squirrels
OMNIVORES
racoons
wood mouse
skunk
box turtle
crow
many birds
warbler
chickadee
woodpeckers
thrush
brown creeper
human beings
wasps
centipedes
carnivorous
beetles
moles
toad shrews
salamanders
snakes
DECOMPOSERS
bacteria
fungi
earthworms
millipedes
springtails
sowbugs
fly & beetle
larvae
slug.
ANIMAL EATERS
(Carnivores)
gray horned
owl
fox
coyote
weasel
fisher
bobcat

FERNS

see Interrupted Fern (Roadside)

BOULDER SUCCESSION

FOREST

F. tiny tree

E. fern

D. moss

C. foliose lichen

B. crustose lichen

A - bare rock

and ferns. This succession of soil-building plants can be seen again on the erratic boulders strewn over the forest floor, where the soil is being carefully built, first by crustose lichens, then by foliose lichens. The mosses follow where enough organic debris is accumulated. Here and there a fern may grow out of the moss mat or from a crack in the rock with organic matter in it. And one day a tiny fir, pine or maple seedling may root in the rock-borne bedding. One boulder can hold all these stages, the steeper, more exposed face bearing the lichen pioneers, the pockets of debris holding the young seedlings. Here is the history of the forest in miniature.

Our forests are very important to us. We must cut wood carefully in them, never leaving the soil bare to be washed away, never compacting it with heavy vehicles.① This forest cover helps to absorb the water of our heavy rains and snows, providing us with fresh ground water that would otherwise run off quickly, taking soil with it, silting and flooding rivers and causing later droughts. The forest moderates the climate with the moisture that is transpired from its leaves, cooling the air in the summer, and evening-out the seasons' temperature just as evaporation from the ocean does. We are protected from extreme heat, cold and dryness. We must be sure that we do not destroy animal habitats or cause an imbalance in the numbers of animals by indiscriminate hunting or use of pesticides. We need the water, soil, air, food and materials that the forests provide.

Pipsissewa

white-pink

6"

(July-Aug)

Rattle-snake roots

2-5'

(Sept.Oct)

White lettuce

Gall-of-the-earth

white flowers

Whorled wood aster

1-3'

(Sept.Oct)

① compacted soil has no air in it and cannot absorb water. It cannot support a protective plant cover and so is easily washed away.

LATER FOREST FLOWERS

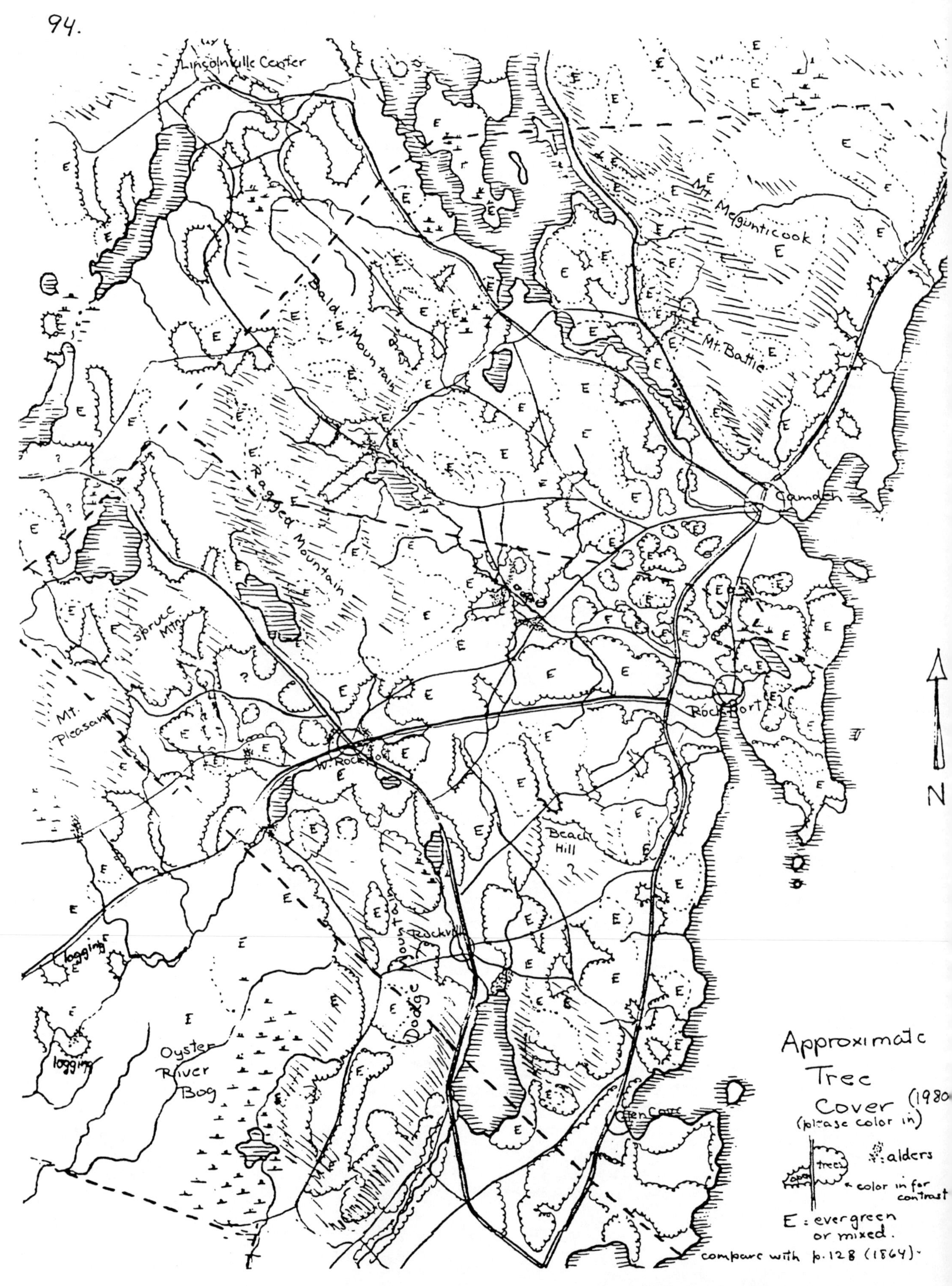
Lincolnville Center
Mt. Megunticook
Bald Mountain
Mt. Battie
Camden
Ragged Mountain
Spruce Mtn.
Mt. Pleasant
Rockport
W. Rockport
Beach Hill
logging
Oyster River Bog
Dodge Mountain
Rockville
Glen Cove
N
Approximate Tree Cover (1980)
(please color in)
trees
alders
color in for contrast
E: evergreen or mixed.
compare with p. 128 (1864).

MOUNTAIN LEDGE

There are many ledges of bare exposed rock on the Camden Hills. They were scraped smooth by the weight of the last glacier that poured over these mountains. The hills themselves are not very high (Mt. Battie is under 800 feet above sea level, Mt. Megunticook is almost 1,400 feet, Ragged Mtn.: 1,300 ft. and Bald Mtn.: 1,270 ft.), not high enough to create a subarctic environment like that of mountain tops above the tree line ① But the ledges are bare of soil, exposed to harsh, cold, drying winds in the winter, to the prying effects of ice, the burning sun and beating rain. Only very hardy plants live there, and not many animals. The ledges look as though they are above the tree line even though they're not.

As you emerge from the wooded slope of Mt. Battie and scramble up up the ledge, all the plants seem to huddle closer to the ground. Wherever there is enough soil between the rocks, scrubby red oaks grow up, the same kind as the tall trees in the woods but on Mt. Battie they are bent by the wind and stunted. Their leaves near the ground are large and spreading to catch the light, while the leaves on the upper branches are small and spiky to avoid drying out. There are a few small red (Norway) pines, able to grow on the ledge better than the Eastern white pine of the richer woods. Their roots must spread far over the rocks to get a grip

① the tree line here would be at about 6,000 ft. for our latitude.

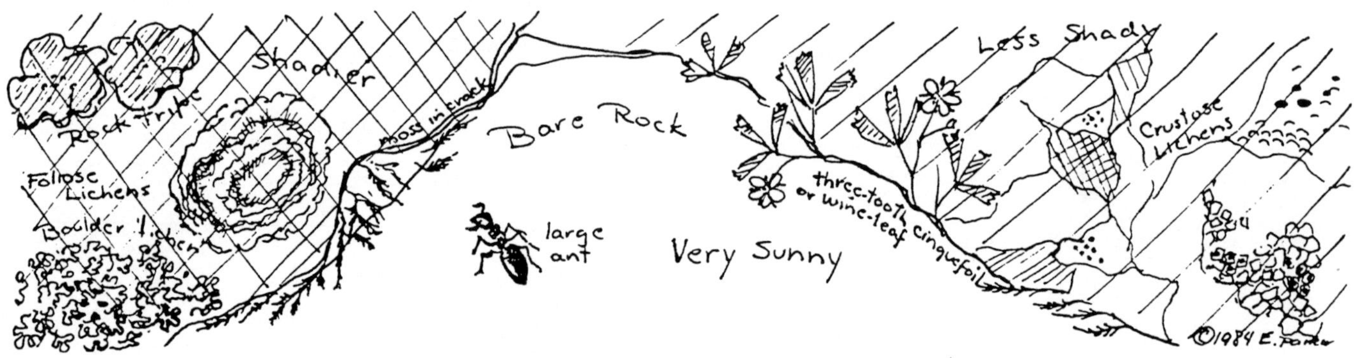

and find water and soil. Some of the trees have died and left their branches stark and gray against the sky, bare as drift wood: wood-rotting organisms cannot break them down in such dry bright places, so only the wind and rain can work on them.

Among the small shrubs are the pin or fire cherry, that thrives on burned-over ground, and some bayberry, that withstands salty air. These plants cannot stand the competition of other plants, but here there is little competition. There is spreading dwarf juniper, prick-needled, with pale green berries(2); shiny bearberry, with mealy red berries, and mats of broom crowberry (Corema), like tiny spruce branches, all lying low on the ground. There are low-bush blueberries, some huckleberries, and an occasional sheeps laurel (lamb kill)(3). Chokeberry bushes are everywhere. and three-toothed cinquefoils grow in the smaller crevices, looking like dried-up strawberry plants. All of these plants are adapted in two important ways to the environment: they have leaves that are small or waxy and don't easily dry

(2) Juniper berries are used flavor gin.
(3) because it is poisonous to sheep.

and they are low-lying plants which cannot easily be blown away.

The rocks themselves are not completely bare. On rock faces that are shaded part of the day, low crustose lichens are growing[4]; they appear as areas of different shades of gray with edges like the borders of countries on a map or areas of gray "mud cracks" with black fruiting dots or small patches of bright yellow-green and bright orange-green boulder lichen that spreads like tree rings in different shades. There are some patches of rock tripe, a foliose lichen, like black, crackly dried leaves attached to the rock[5]. On some sheltered ledges that are flatter and more moist, there are mats of spongy reindeer lichen and cloud lichen, like tiny silvery-white trees.

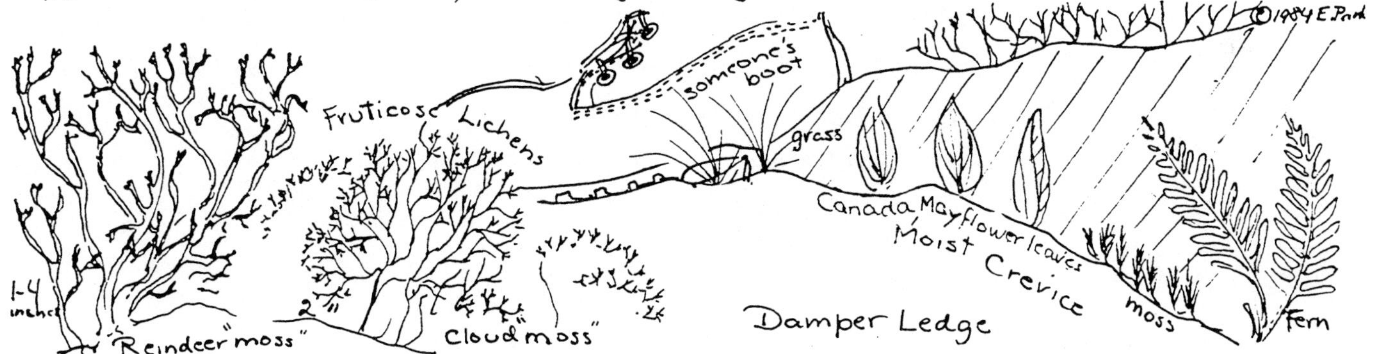

These lichens can withstand the harsh climate. The tough fungi protect the photosynthesizing algae inside. Their spongy cover absorbs water in wet weather and prevents its loss in dry weather. The lichens are pioneers on the barren rock ledges, just as their ancestors were on the bare early land, slowly breaking down the surface of the rock while they live off the food provided by their captive algae. The lichens help form a thin base of soil for higher plants to live on; the moss that hangs out of a shady crack will come next.

There are few flying insects or small birds on the ledge. They would be blown away too easily. An occasional ant can be seen scurrying across the rock, or a grasshopper in warm weather. Strong winged hawks[6] soar overhead, riding on the rising currents of warm air and watching for small birds and other prey farther down the hills. This is a world of rock and crouching plants— not a rich enough hunting ground for animal life.

(4) "Crusty texture as opposed to foliose (leafy) and fruticose (fruited) lichens.
(5) These can be eaten as survival food.
(6) Hawks over the mountain - red-shouldered, broadwing, red tail, sharp shin, Cooper's, goshawk - immature bald eagle - (over Bald Mtn). Also, turkey vultures on Bald Mtn.

ROADSIDES + FIELDS - disturbed environments.

When we walk along a country road, or look out of the window of a car, we see plants along the roadside, in the ditch, up the bank of the road and a little way into any fields that border the road. This is the most that many of us see of wild plants and animals.

The roadside and field might both be called "disturbed environments" because they are formed when human beings disrupt the soil, drainage system & plants that are natural to the area. In making a road, we dig out some parts and build up other parts. We dig drainage ditches along the side and make a hard, impermeable, heat-absorbing surface on the top. In making a field, we often do little more than cut down trees to let grasses grow in the sun. Sometimes we plow and seed it for hay or crops ①, and even use herbicides and pesticides to make sure that only the plants we want will grow there.

In both cases, we have changed the environment and as a result, the plants and animals that can live there also change. If we had done nothing, there would still be mixed forest of leafy deciduous trees and needled coniferous trees because that is the kind of vegetation that naturally grows in the soils of our climate (cold, below-freezing winters with 40-50 inches average yearly rainfall). If we do nothing more, the mixed forest will slowly return, shading out the sun-loving field plants. (Sunny fields or clearings are also created naturally by forest fires.)

Many of the plants (c. 50%) that live by our roadsides and in our fields are not native American plants. They have followed the Europeans and their agriculture from its origins in the Near East, for as long as 12,000 years. We tend to call these plants "weeds", because they spring up quickly in disturbed ground without being planted by us, and they often interfere with our crops. The colonists from Europe brought some of these weed seeds unintentionally in their belongings. These plants are sun-loving and particularly tough. Their seeds germinate quickly in the trail of disturbed soil that we leave - and this is why we see them along the roadside.

TOUGH LOW PLANTS on the HARD-PACKED SHOULDER

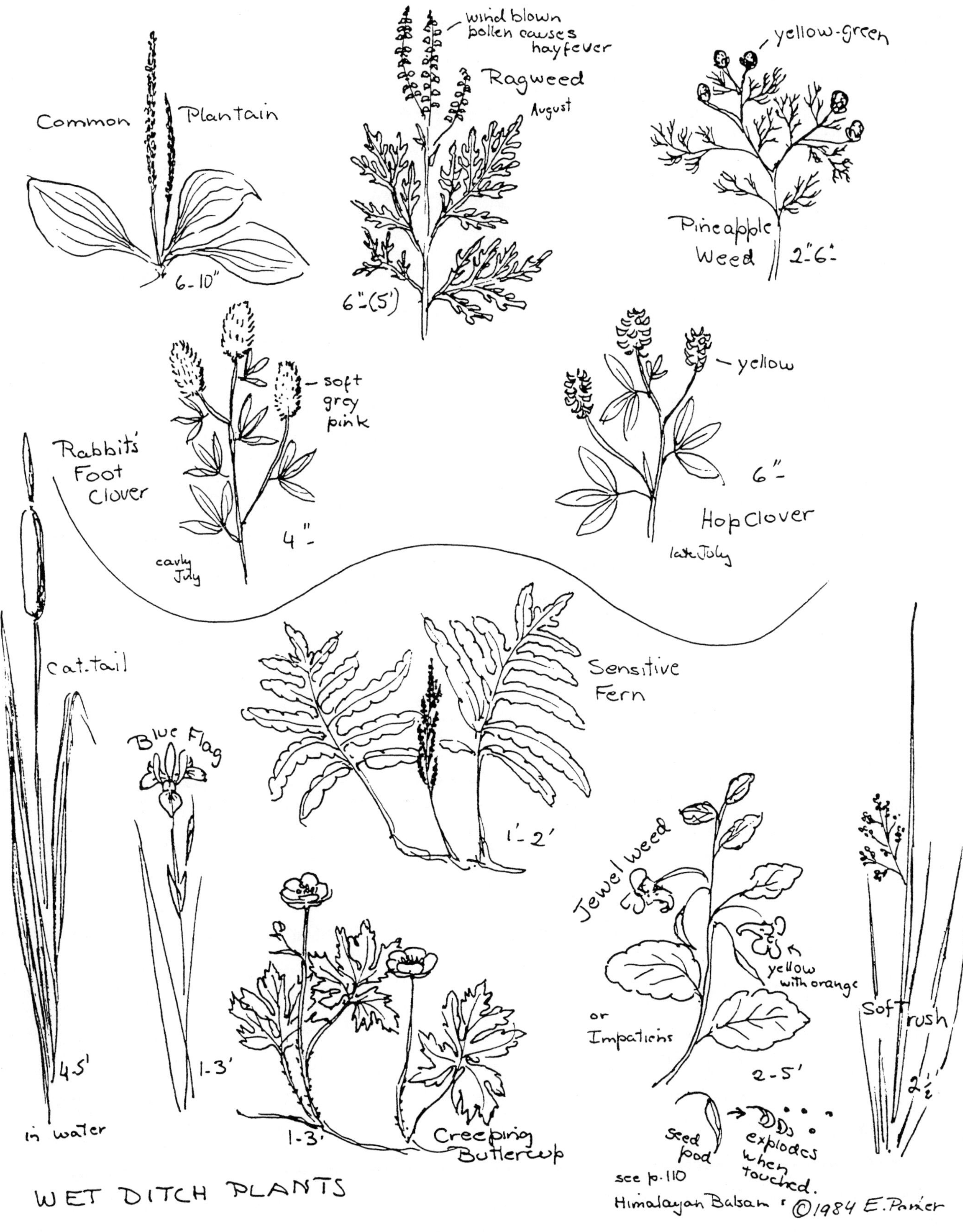

WET DITCH PLANTS

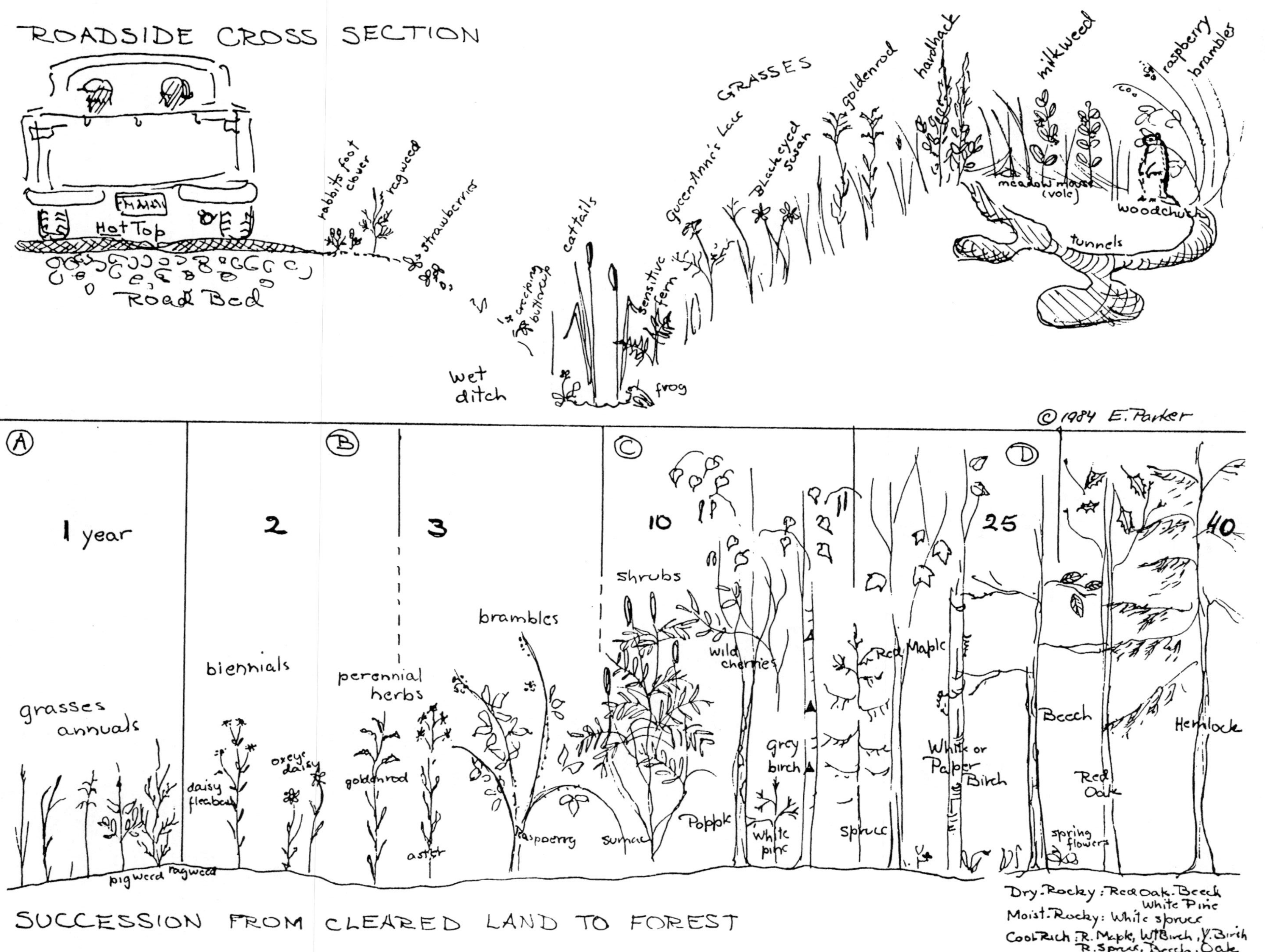
ROADSIDE CROSS SECTION
Hot Top
Road Bed
rabbits foot clover
ragweed
strawberries
creeping buttercup
wet ditch
cattails
frog
sensitive fern
Queen Anne's Lace
GRASSES
Black eyed Susan
goldenrod
hardhack
milkweed
meadow mouse (vole)
raspberry brambles
woodchuck
tunnels
© 1984 E. Parker
A
1 year
grasses annuals
pigweed
ragweed
2
biennials
daisy fleabane
oxeye daisy
B
3
perennial herbs
goldenrod
aster
brambles
raspberry
C
10
shrubs
sumac
Popple
wild cherries
grey birch
white pine
spruce
Red Maple
White or Paper Birch
D
25
Beech
Red Oak
spring flowers
40
Hemlock
Dry. Rocky: Red Oak. Beech White Pine
Moist. Rocky: White spruce
Cool Rich: R. Maple, Wt Birch, Y. Birch R. Spruce, Beech. Oak
SUCCESSION FROM CLEARED LAND TO FOREST

Here is a short list of these European & Asian plants, our followers: witch grass, plantain (called "white man's footsteps"), Queen Anne's lace (wild carrot); dandelion, burdock, mullein, yarrow, oxeye daisy, sow-thistle, St. Johnswort, hop clover, sweet clover, tansy.

Not all our wayside plants came in the last few hundred years. Many are native Americans: milkweed, the goldenrods, most of the asters, lupins, sunflowers, black-eyed Susan, jewelweed, evening primrose... The farther back from the road you walk, the more native plants you find.

All these plants need sun. We cut back the forest and this huge variety of sun-loving plants spring up – many more kinds than grow in the forest. The roadside has several different environments; dry, wet, fertile, sterile.

On the hard-packed, gravelly shoulder of the road you will see plants that can stand being walked on, driven over, and parched by the extreme heat radiating from the blacktop. They must be resistant to road salt, exhaust fumes and oil spills. They must be able to get nourishment from poor soil. On the portion that is "scraped" by the snow plow, a tough, sparse grass spreads. Soft, fuzzy grey rabbit-foot clover lines the road in mid-July and is replaced by yellow hop clover by August. Other plants are plantain, pineapple weed, knotweed, cudweed, shepherd's purse, ragweed (because of the heat from the black top) and, sometimes wild strawberries.

In the wet ditch by the road, where all the run off from the pavement must go, you see plants that like moist habitats or even marshes: jewelweed (in shadier places), sensitive fern, creeping buttercup, and blue flag (iris) and cattails in the wettest places, with rushes and sedges. (see Purple Loosestrife p. 110)

Up the sunny bank beside the road, masses of wildflowers grow, if the bank is not mowed too often and is not heavily eroded. This is a very long list: lupins, dandelions, strawberries, oxeye daisies, daisy fleabane, cowvetch, red clover, day lilies, goat's beard, Queen Anne's lace, hawkweeds, milkweed, tansy, yarrow, evening primrose, mullein, goldenrod, sunflowers, asters and many different kinds of grasses. There are clumps of shrubs and young trees springing up:

Dandelion

Strawberry

Violets

Poison Ivy

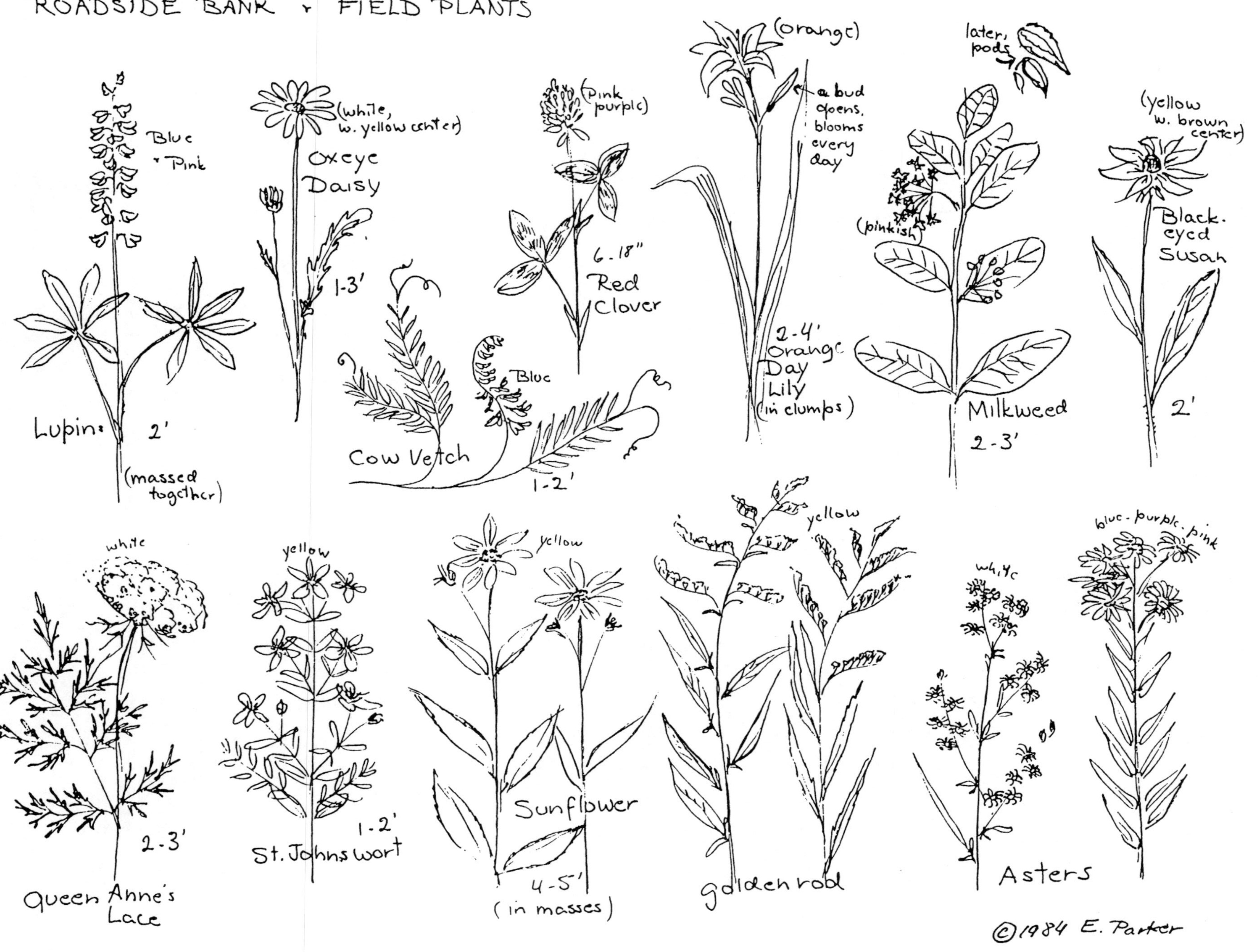
ROADSIDE BANK + FIELD PLANTS
Blue + Pink
Lupine
2'
(massed together)
(white, w. yellow center)
Oxeye Daisy
1-3'
Cow Vetch
Blue
1-2'
(Pink purple)
6-18"
Red Clover
(orange)
a bud opens, blooms every day
2-4'
Orange Day Lily
(in clumps)
later, pods
(pinkish)
Milkweed
2-3'
(yellow w. brown center)
Black-eyed Susan
2'
white
2-3'
Queen Anne's Lace
yellow
1-2'
St. Johns wort
yellow
Sunflower
4-5'
(in masses)
yellow
goldenrod
white
blue-purple-pink
Asters

sumac, raspberry + blackberry brambles, wild rose, arrowwood, red-osier dogwood, yound choke cherries + blackcherries, (with black knot fungus in them often), common elderberry and, sometimes, young popple (quaking aspen) trees. Here and there are old apple trees.

On <u>shady banks</u>, over hung by woods, there are more ferns, mosses, woodland floor plants like bunchberry, patches of coltsfoot (in gravelly places), violets and poison ivy.

In the <u>fields</u>, back from the road, grow many of the "sunny bank" plants, the variety depending on how often the field is mowed or cut back and on what the soil and drainage is like. You might see masses of milkweed, sometimes dogbane: patches of wild strawberry, clumps of hardhack (steeplebush), tangles of bedstraw, of stitchwort (chickweed) and yellow rattle - ①. Where the land has been filled or packed down, as in a vacant lot or abandoned workarea, there may be tall mugwort, fireweed, sweet clover, mullein, burdock, thistle; here the ground is moist, there will be sedges and violets, and along small streams and ditches, there will be shrubby willows, (pussy willow + others) and alder thickets ②.

Always the forest is trying to grow back to the "climax" condition of mixed hardwoods and coniferous trees that are native to Maine. This happens in very much the same way it would if there had been a fire in the forest. Ⓐ First the grasses and annual "weeds" move in, the same plants that sprout from seeds quickly and need sun. Ⓑ Then come perennial herbs and grasses, golden rods, asters . . . . and brambles (raspberries and blackberries). Ⓒ After 10 years or less, you will see stands of sumac, next page

. . . .

① "yellow rattle", because the seeds rattle in the dry pods.

② The hated alder can fix nitrogen like a legume and is important in erosion and flood control.

yellow
Evening Primrose. 1-4'
burrs
2-5'
Burdock

ROADSIDE & FIELD

popples, fire or pin cherry and black cherry, grey birch (the very white kind that doesn't peel). Ashes, white pine move in, followed by maples. The last trees to establish themselves are the slow-growing oaks and beeches that cast a solid shade, and in some places, stands of spruce. And so a forest has grown again. Parts of this sequence can be seen on the road side and in the field. Areas that are going through these successional stages are important to wild life because of the many berries, seeds and tender leaves (see FOREST)

If you are in a car, most of the animals you notice will be dead ones, killed by other cars. The road, beside disturbing the natural drainage of the land and contributing to erosion and flooding, makes a barrier in the world of the animals that live in the forest and field. They often try to cross it unsuccessfully.

Crow at road-side

You will see skunk, raccoon, porcupine, woodchuck, toads, chipmunk, turtles, grouse, snakes, song-birds, dogs and cats that have been hit by cars. The most frequent live animal is the crow who comes to take what it can of the remains. The crow is wise enough to fly up when a car comes, but these other animals are either too slow or blinded by car lights or confused by the speed of the approaching car.

If you are walking along the road in the summer, you will see insects eating the roadside plants. Band-winged grasshoppers crouch, invisible, on the road-shoulder and fly up with rattling wings as you approach, to land nearby, invisible again. Ants scurry about on the sandy edge. Many of the insects in the grass and flowers are adapted to eat only one kind of plant. There are Monarch butterfly caterpillars in the milkweed, Sulphurs in the clover, cabbage butterflies on mustard (cabbage) family plants, tiny beetles in goldenrod. In the grasses and on weed stems, you will

Band-winged grasshopper (locust)
1.2"
Flies up by roadside

see the foam of spittle bug nymphs, hiding in the wet bubbles that protect their soft bodies from drying out. Fat grasshoppers and tiny leaf hoppers fly up and disappear as you push through the grass into the field. On the goldenrod stems you may see the swollen galls where a tiny gall insect has laid its eggs and the plant has over-reacted around them, forming a nest for the larva.

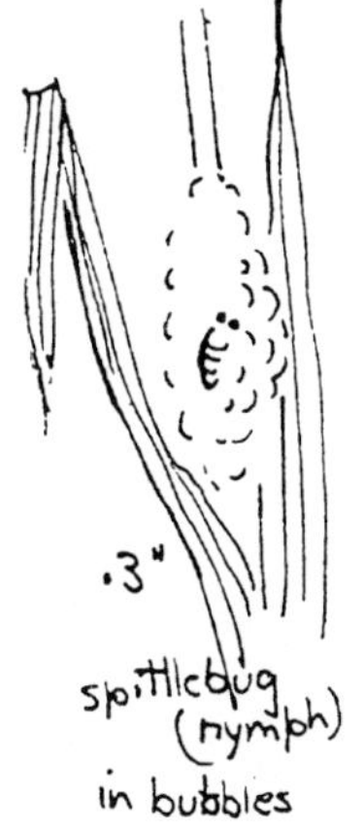

spittlebug (nymph) in bubbles

In the young cherry trees by the road, there may be tent caterpillars defoliating the tree by day and returning to their tent nests at night. In the fall, there may be banded woolybear caterpillars, foolishly trying to cross the road. On warm days and nights in in the late summer, you will hear the singing insects in the grasses, the males of each species making their special signal to attract a female of the same kind. Some of the songs are of:

Field cricket

meadow grasshoppers — long buzzes separated by "zips" = "bzzzz, zip-zip-zip-zip-bzzzz.."
field crickets - "cricket" - "cricket" (chirps)
tiny crickets - shrill "prrrrr....."

goldfinch 4½-6"

There are birds eating the grass seeds, other seeds and the insects: song sparrows, a cat bird in the shrubs, gold finch on the thistle heads. Red-wing blackbirds are stationed in the cat-tails, each male a respectable distance from the next along the road, maintaining their territories. Swallows swoop after flying insects and gather in the late summer on the telephone wires before flying south for the winter. In a wet meadow, there might be nesting killdeer that cry out in shrill voices as they fly, sometimes in the night. Hordes of robins feed by the road in the early spring when they first arrive and before they establish their territories.

Red-winged Blackbird 9-10"

Hidden down in the grasses of the field are the meadow-

ROADSIDE SHRUBS & YOUNG TREES

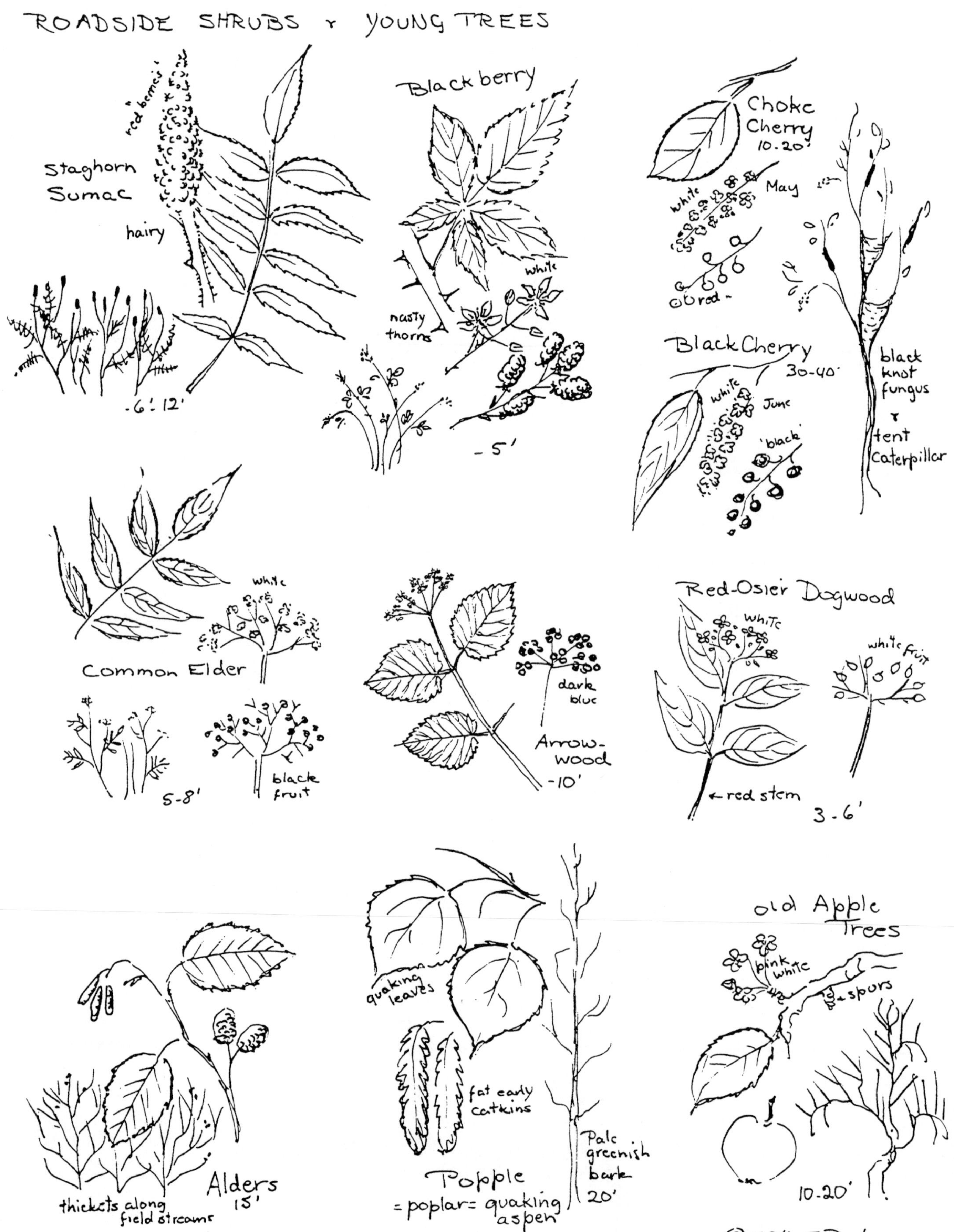

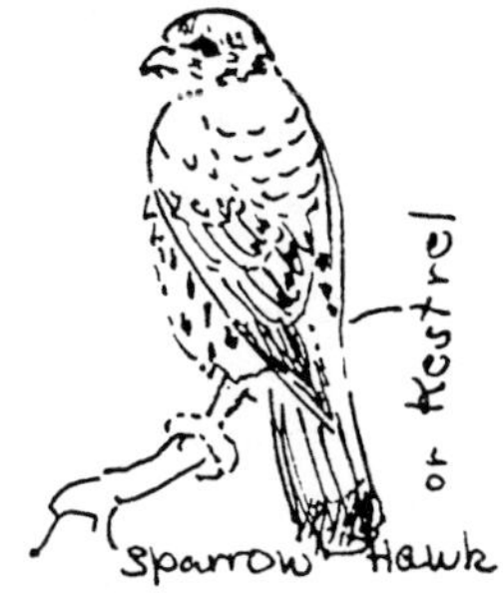

mice (voles), whose tunnels in the grass may be seen in the spring when the snow melts. There are kangaroo mice too, and tiny short-tail shrew that devour insects constantly. Garter snakes eat the mice and earthworms, and frogs in the ditch. The earthworms are working away (if the soil is not too wet or acid) aerating and enriching the soil. They are also eaten by moles under the ground.

Norway rats (also "people-followers" from Europe) haunt the banks and fields, adapted to eat anything they can find: small animals, insects, wildfruit, seeds and bits of human garbage. Fat woodchuck dig burrows in the field, eating clover, grasses & weeds. The little brown bat flits over the field in the early dusk, eating flying insects as the swallows do by day. The deer venture out to browse in the evening, on shrub tips and fallen apples.

4" meadow mouse (or vole)

These animals are hunted by other animals. The sparrow hawk perches on an electric wire, watching for rodents, small birds & large insects The red fox comes at dusk, hunting rodents, birds, eggs, grasshoppers and foraging berries and seeds. Skunks and raccoons hunt mice, frogs, eggs, insects, berries, seeds, roots & grubs (the skunk). And in the fall hunting season, men are seen in red caps, flushing out game birds

The roadside varies in color and texture through the year as different plants green, flower and die back. There are the first green daylily spears & pussywillow buds in March & April, the yellow of dandelions in May, blue of lupins in June and blowing white daisies, orange of daylilies in July & goldenrod yellows starting in August, aster blues & whites in September,

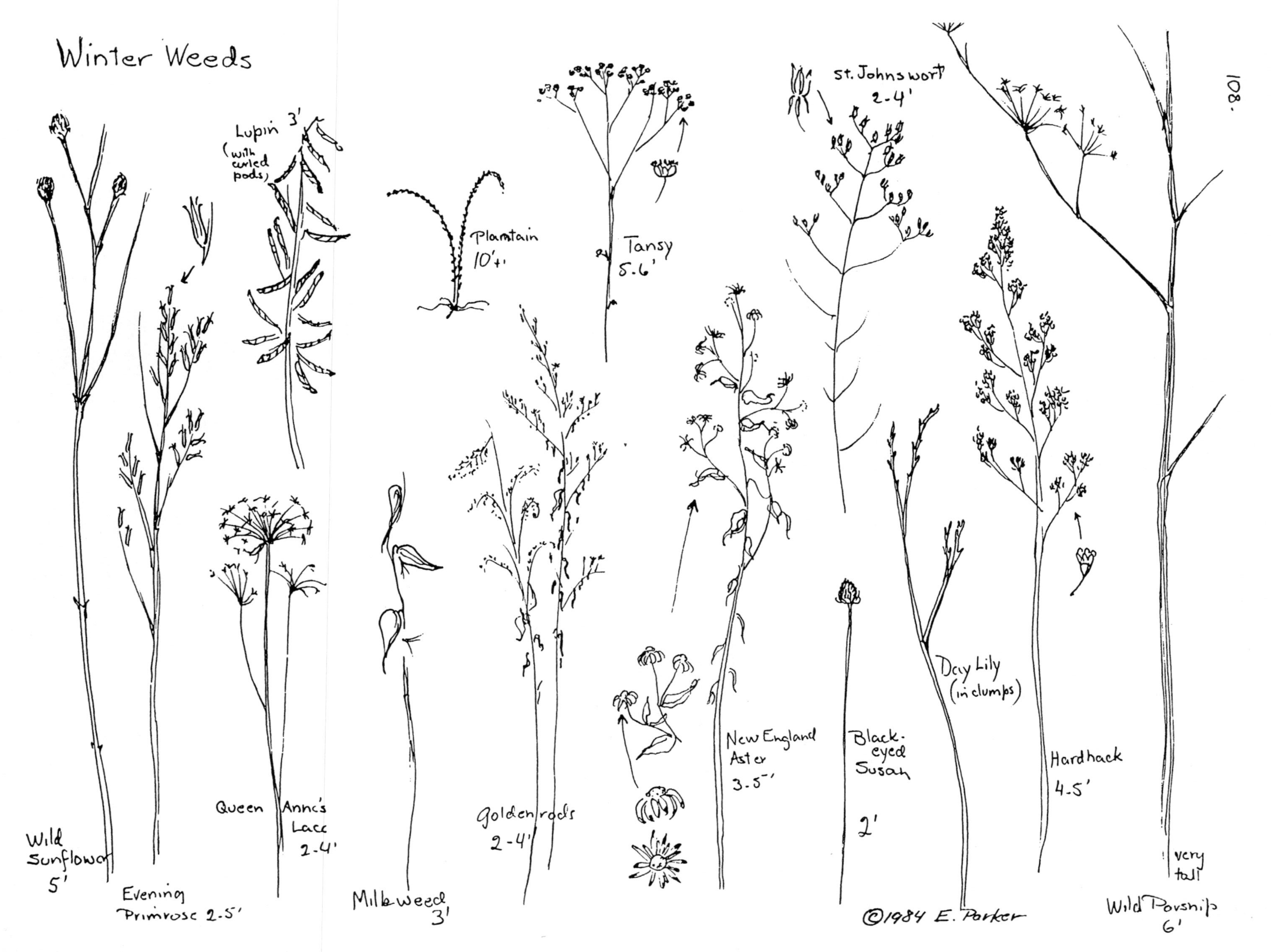
Winter Weeds
Wild Sunflower 5'
Evening Primrose 2-5'
Lupin 3' (with curled pods)
Queen Anne's Lace 2-4'
Plantain 10"+
Milkweed 3'
Tansy 5-6'
Goldenrods 2-4'
New England Aster 3-5'
St. Johnswort 2-4'
Black-eyed Susan 2'
Day Lily (in clumps)
Hardhack 4-5'
very tall
Wild Parsnip 6'
©1984 E. Parker

ROADSIDE CALENDAR

	1st week	2nd week	3rd week	4th week
March	sap buckets MUD SEASON	some pussy willows out	geese arrive	day lily sprouts popple buds big
April	killdeer cry cat bird back	hordes of robins catkins in popple	dandelion greens tansy leaves strawberry leaves red-wing blackbird	ants out along road (little sand hills) bees in the willow flowers
May	violets ← spring peepers in wet places	DANDELIONS (YELLOW) bloom ferns up choke cherry bloom trees leafing	strawberry flowers red elderberry flowers	tent caterpillars at work. APPLE BLOSSOMS
June	spittlebug foam buttercup bl. forget-me-nots GRASSES BLOOMING (hay fever)	stitchwort flowering	LUPINS (BLUE + PINK) bloom Blue vetch bl. DAISIES ROSES	STRAWBERRIES RIPE red clover blooms
July	Valerian bl. orange DAYLILIES bloom goatsbeard seed head	Rabbit-foot clover on roadside → Queen Anne's Lace MILKWEED blooms Black-eyed Susan Daisy Fleabane St. Johnswort	Raspberries ripe	Hopclover on roadside Blueberries →
August	←	Jewel weed bl Blackberries ← INSECTS SINGING →	red Sumac heads GOLDEN ROD bloom	WILD SUNFLOWER yellow Hawkweeds (YELLOW) →
Sept.	swallows begin to leave	ASTERS (WHITE + BLUE) bloom → insects sing till black frost →		Red Maple, poison ivy + blueberry turn red
Oct.	Geese going First frosts ←	tree leaves down bird HUNTERS OUT →		Milkweed seed blowing
Nov.	Hard frosts (black)	grasses lie down - meadow mouse tunnels + holes in grass seed heads of asters - golden rod (with galls) tansy - evening primrose hardhack - milkweed - Lupin Queen Annes Lace		
The Rest of the Winter	animal tracks in snow			

in October the fall colors of the red maple, red blueberry plants and poison ivy. And after that, all that is left are the weed stalks and seed heads, and tracks in the snow.

There are several kinds of environmental problems that arise on the roadside. In the spring thaw and during rainstorms, enormous run-off from the road can wash the side of the road away and erode the bank over the ditch, carrying silt into streams and suffocating the water life. The impermeable road cannot absorb water, and disturbed soil does not hold it well either. Drainage is often poorly planned with water backing up or flowing too fast and causing flooding. If the roadsides or fields are sprayed, the wildlife is slowly poisoned, with the resulting disappearance of some insects, the birds that eat them, and the animals and birds that eat them in turn, especially the hawks. If the road is salted in the winter, this salt is washed off into the roadside where it kills plants and soaks into the watertable, contaminating nearby wells. We must consider carefully before we build new roads because of their drastic effect on the land they are built on and on the plants and animals that live there.

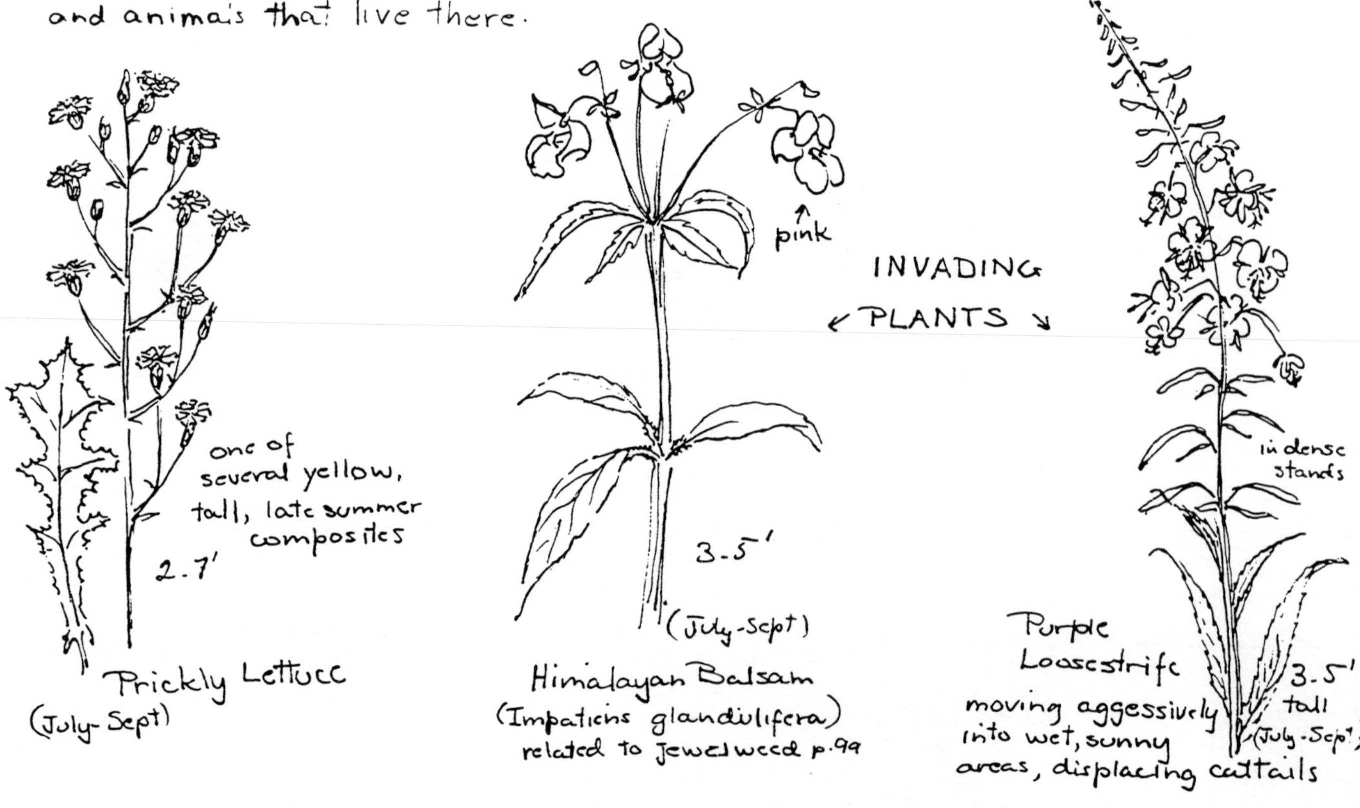

HUMAN USE OF LOCAL NATURAL RESOURCES: CULTURE

Living things vary in their ability to adjust to different habitats. Some plants and animals can only live in one special kind of place: the periwinkle can only live on the wave-washed rocks on the edge of the cold sea. The tiny sundew plant can only live in acid wet places where other plants can't compete with it. Some creatures, animals in particular, can adapt to a fairly wide range of conditions, finding different kinds of food in different places. Most of these wide-ranging animals are omnivorous (eating plants and animals), or scavengers (eating dead and living food). Racoons are such animals; so are Norway rats and herring gulls. Human beings also have this ability to adjust.

Human beings are able to make a living in a wide range of habitats, by changing their eating habits and by using different materials for shelter, clothing and tools, according to what is available. They also are able to alter their environment considerably to suit their purposes. Like other animals, they alter their environment unintentionally as well, sometimes destroying the habitat that sustains them.

Over the thousands of years that human beings have existed, they have discovered different ways of making use of their environment. The knowledge of these ways is passed from generation to generation within each group of people. These ways are called the peoples' "culture". We have had several different "cultures" in this area - sometimes co-existing - sometimes one displacing and destroying another.

Native Americans

The first human beings to make use of the natural resources of our area were probably people who followed the return of vegetation north after

CULTURE

the glaciers retreated.[1] Humans had come from Asia to North and South America about 40 to 30 thousand years ago. Remains of their fires, stone tools and bones and shells of their animal prey have been found in other parts of the Americas. They certainly also gathered plants to eat and to use to make nets and containers, but nothing remains of the plant materials. Probably these Paleo-Indians, as they are now called, came to Maine from the South and West between 13,000 and 8,000 years ago. From that time on, different peoples, or, at least, peoples who left somewhat different rubbish behind for archeologists to find, have lived in Maine. The Paleo people hunted large mammals and left behind long graceful fluted spear-points. From 10,000 y.a.[2] to 4,500 y.a., the "Archaic" people, who hunted smaller game after the large mammals were killed off, left smaller points and ground stone tools. A later people left red ochre (iron oxide[3]) paint in their cemeteries, so we call them "Red Paint" people (4,500 - 3,800 y.a.) Another group cremated their dead and resembled people living in the Susquehanna valley in Pennsylvania, so they are named "Susquehanna" (3,800 - 3,400 y.a.). From about 2,300 y.a., the people living here began making pottery out of the clays they found. About 1,000 y.a., they began to cultivate a few plants as crops. They were known as "Woodland" Indians" because they lived in the forested east coast and they were probably the same Native

2-3" fluted spear point

Paleo- 10,000 B.P.

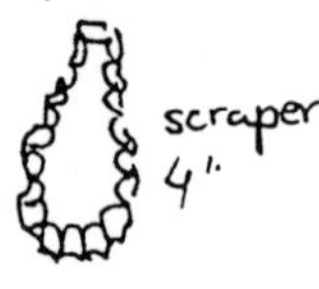

scraper 4"

point 2"

Archaic > 5,000 B.P.

plummet 2"

4" woman's knife

5" grooved ax head

drill-point

Some stone tools of Paleo- & Archaic Peoples (twine, wood bark & leather don't keep)

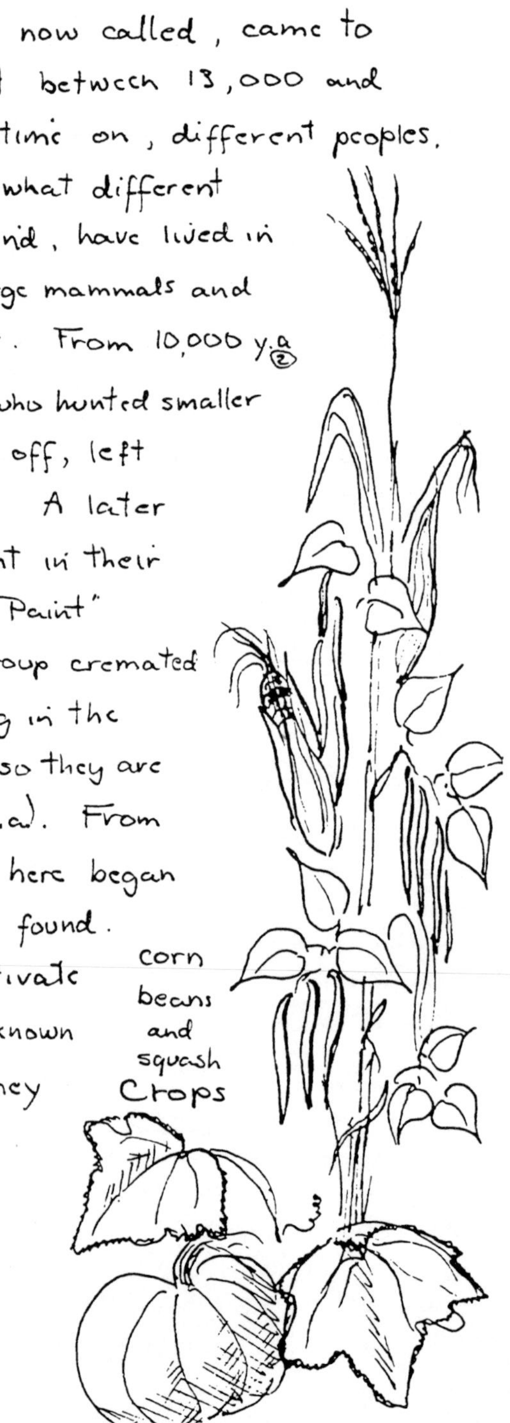

corn beans and squash Crops

[1] see Time Line [2] y.a. = years ago

[3] from Mt. Kathadin.

from Kroeber - Natural & Cultural Areas of Native North America. 1939

American(1) peoples encountered by the European explorers in the 1500's and possibly by earlier Vikings.

The people who made their living by the streams, woods and bays of Camden and Rockport were of the Eastern Abenaki(2) culture and language group of the great Algonquin peoples who live across the north of the U.S. and Canada, mostly in the woods and lakes left by the glaciers. Tribes occupied river valleys or drainage systems, the water divide between the river systems serving as a rough boundary. The rivers were used for transportation and defined the territory.(3)

The St. George river valley was occupied by the Wawenok of the Kennebec group; the Penobscot Bay and river was the territory of the Penobscot people. Beyond, to the east were the Passamaquoddy in the St. Croix river valley, and the Malecite in the St. John river valley(4)

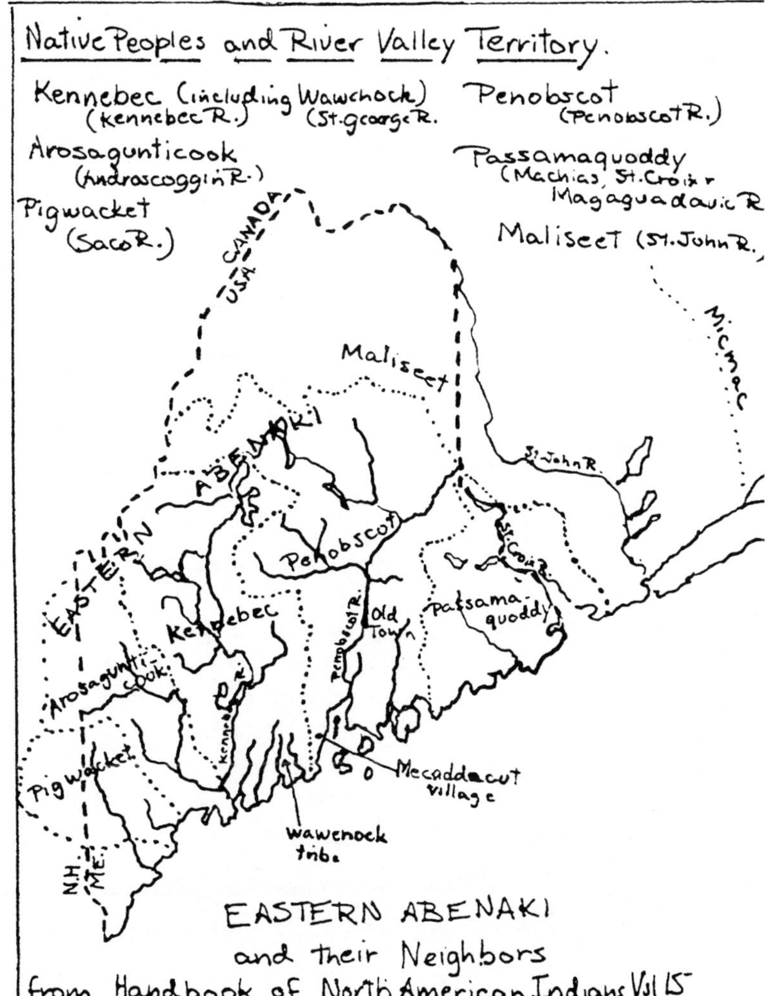

EASTERN ABENAKI and their Neighbors
from Handbook of North American Indians Vol 15

(1) the term "Native American" is used instead of 'Indian', to correct the confusion caused by Columbus who thought he had reached the Indies.

(2) Abenaki: "easterner".

(3) see map of Major Watersheds

(4) Malecite were called "Etchemins" by the early explorers while the Micmacs, who live in Nova Scotia & New Brunswick were called "Tarratines"

CULTURE

The population would have been very low in our area, compared to now, possibly several dozen people and certainly no more than 200, and that according to season. Captain John Smith, in 1614, reported a village that was probably in Camden called "Mecaddacut". Other names, reported by the early explorers, for our region and mountains are: Megunticook, Medumcook, Bedabedec & Medembettox (which sounds like Mt. Battie even though it's supposed to be Dodge Mountain in Rockland).

The people who lived here may have migrated seasonally, moving inland in the winter, to hunt, and fish through the ice, and coming back to the shore and the islands in the summer to gather shellfish and crustaceans & to catch fish in their weirs. These native peoples made efficient and careful use of their surroundings. Their food, materials for clothing, shelter and tools all came from this region. They found the things they needed in the forest, rivers, marshes, mud flats and rocky shore. The things that they traded, like red iron oxide from Katahdin, fine stone spear points and ornaments - were not necessary for survival.

Many of their needs were supplied by the plants of the area. The women and children gathered these for the group to eat.① Some of the food plants growing here are: cattails[B], providing tubers, stem pith & pollen "flour", bulrush tubers, arrowhead tubers, ground nuts[A] (a kind of wild bean with "roots", Jerusalem artichokes (wild sunflowers with edible tubers), milkweed (young greens, young pods, flowers), skunk cabbage root and young greens, aster and dock greens, sea weed and spring fiddleheads of the ostrich fern.

Cordage Plants

Spruce (root)

Basswood (inner bark) (A)

Indian Hemp? (a Dogbane)

Bulrush

Cattail

① Do not eat these plants unless you know someone who has eaten them and will show you how.
A. mentioned but uncommon
B. common but not mentioned

bucket

dish

rain hat

— Birchbark —

Some Local Edible Plants

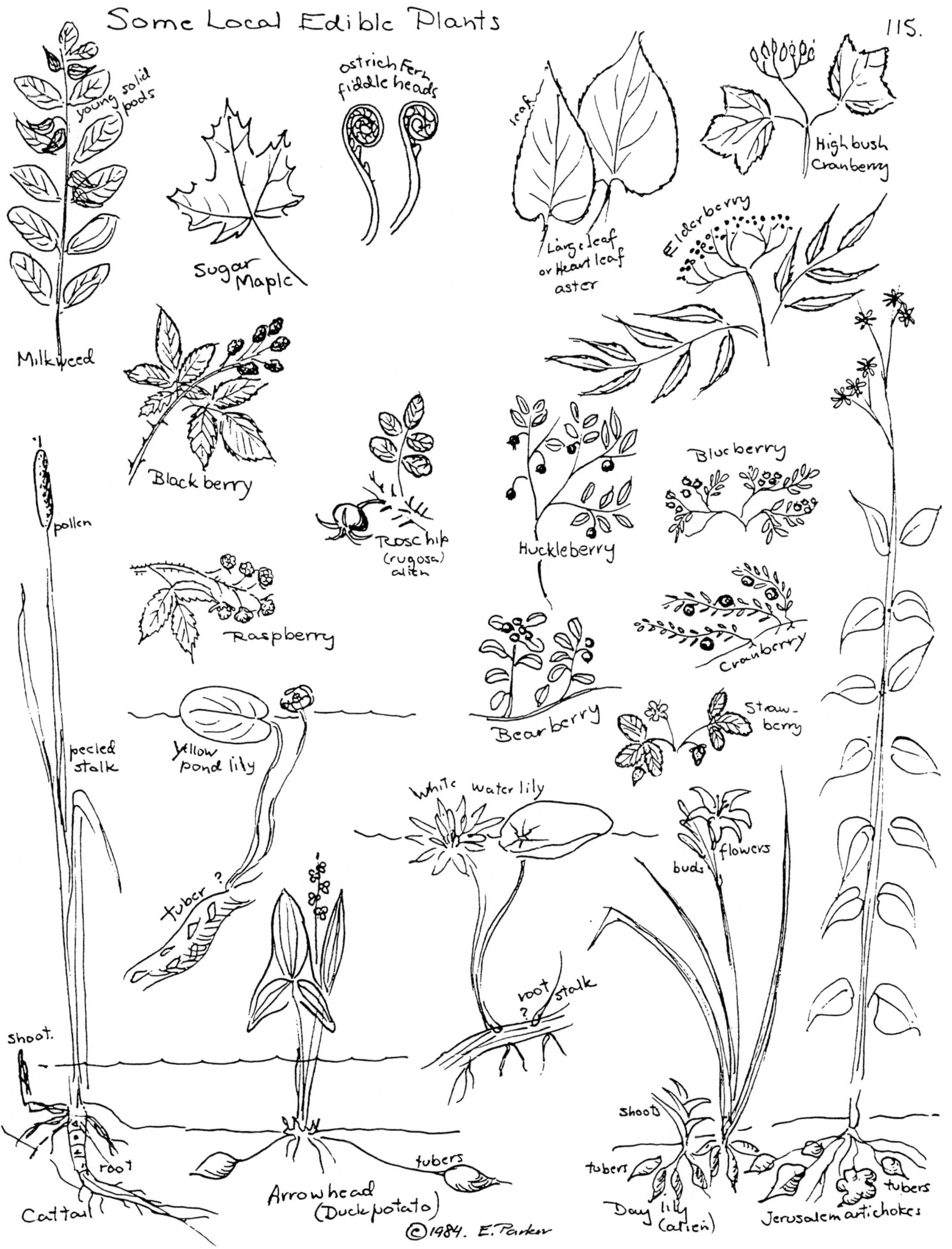

Some Local Edible Wild Plants (probably available to Abenaki)

Latin Name	Name	Part eaten	place found	Season Sp.	Su.	Fa.	Wi.
Acer saccharum	Sugar Maple	sap.	rich woods	x			x
Alaria esculenta	"Kelp"	whole plant	rocky shore				
Almenchior canadensis	Juneberry	fruit	rich woods		x		
Artostaphylos uva-ursi	Bearberry	fruit	ledges		x		
Asclepias syriaca	Milkweed	flowers, shoots, young pods	clearings	x	x		
Aster sp.	Asters (Large leaf esp.)	leaves	rich woods	x	x		
Chondrus crispus	Irish moss	whole plant	rockyshore				
Cornus canadensis	Bunchberry	fruit	woods		x		
Corylus americana	Hazel	nut	open woods			x	
Crataegus sp.	Thornapple, Hawthorne	fruit	open woods			x	
Fagus grandifolia	Beech	nuts	rich woods			x	
Fragaria sp.	Strawberry	fruit	clearings		x		
Gaultheria procumbens	Wintergreen	leaves (tea)	evergreen woods	x	x	x	x
Helianthus tuberosus	Jerusalem artichoke	tuber	clearings	x		x	
Ledum groenlandicum	Labrador Tea	leaves (tea)	bogs	x	x	x	x
Matteuccia pensylvanica	Ostrich fern	fiddleheads	wet woods	x			
Medeola viginiana	Indian Cucumber	tuber	woods	x		x	
Nymphea odorata	White Water Lily	root stalk	shallow ponds	x		x	
Nuphar advena	Yellow Pond Lily	root stalk	shallow ponds	x			x
Parthenocissus quinquefolia	Virginia creeper	stalk + sap	woods				x
Populos tremuloides	Popple *(1)	sap	wood edge	x			
Porphyra sp.	Laver (seaweed)	whole	rocky shore				
Prunus serotinaus	Black cherry	twigs (tea) fruit	woods + edge		x		
Prunus virginiana	Chokecherry	twigs (tea) fruit	wood edge		x		
Rhus typhina	Staghorn Sumac	shoots, fruit	clearings	x	x	x	
Ribes sp.	Currents	fruit	woods		x		
Rosa sp	Rose	fruit	clearings		x	x	
Rubus frondosa	Blackberry	fruit	clearings		x		
Rubus strigosus	Raspberry	fruit	clearings		x		
Rumex crispus	Curled Dock	leaves	clearings	x	x		
Sagitaria latifolia	Arrowhead	root	shallow water	x		x	
Sambucus canadensis	Common Elderberry	fruit	clearing edge			x	
Scirpus validus	Bulrush	root	Shallow water	x			x
Smilacina stellata	False Solomon's Seal	root, shoots	open woods	x		x	
Symplocarpus foetidus	Skunk Cabbage	root, leaves	wet, swamp woods	x			
Tilia americana	Basswood	sap (inner bark)	moist rich woods	x			x
Tsuga canadensis	Hemlock	leaves (tea)	cool woods				x
Typha latifolia	Cattails	root, pith, pollen	pond edge	x	x	x	x
Vaccinium macrocarpum	Blueberry	fruit	ledges-clearings		x		
Vaccinium macrocarpum	Cranberry	fruit	bogs			x	x
Viburnum americanum	Highbush cranberry (2*)	fruit	damp woods			x	
Vitis labrusca	Fox grapes	fruit	woods, stream edge			x	
Rosa Rugosa (alien)	Rugosa rose	fruit	shore			x	
Hemerocallis fulva (alien)	Daylily	tubers		x		x	

1* also Paper Birch - Betula papyrifera and Yellow Birch - Betula lutea

2* also V. lentago - Nannyberry

— other possible plants: sedge tubers, Mountain ash fruits, trillium tuber, lichens, American chestnut

sp. : species (more than one type)

from F. Densmore + Myron Chase

* moose hair was also spun and fashioned into socks.

snow shoe

In the spring they gathered shoots, fiddleheads and greens; in the summer they picked berries, in the fall there were a few kinds of nuts, (hazel and beech). The main staples, roots and tubers, could be dug in the spring and fall, when they are fat and full, and the frost is out of the ground. In the winter, the inner bark of basswood, maple, birch, popple and even hemlock, pine, spruce and tamarack could be eaten as emergency food. And, of course the maples (and birches) were tapped for their sweet sap in late winter. ("Algonquin" means "tree eater" and these people used the trees for food and much else).

fish hook

antler awl

bone needle

shell scraper

The paper birch supplied bark for making canoes, covering their houses, for water-tight containers and rain gear. Winter teas were made from evergreen needles. Cords and netting were made from twisted fibers of basswood innerbark, dogbane, moosewood and spruce and tamarack roots. Medicines and smoking tobacco came from various plants. Bows were made from ash, oak or maple, arrow shafts from arrowwood (a viburnum shrub). Peat moss provided diapers and dressing for wounds.

eel

grouse

duck

Animals also provided food and materials for the Abenaki. Their clothes were made from skins: kilts, leggings, breech clout for men, shirts or tunics for women. Heavier boots for winter were made of moosehide*. Twisted strips of rabbit skin were made into warm jackets for children. Skins were used to make bags, animal bladders to store some foods (fats). Moose hide was used to cover quickly-made canoes that were later dismantled.

goose

porcupine

Here is a list of some of the animal foods they ate.
birds eggs, game birds (partridge, duck, shorebirds),

bear

snowshoe hare

moose

moose, bear, deer, muskrat, woodchuck, snowshoe hare, beaver, seal, porpoise, alewife, eels, salmon, cod, clams, mussels, periwinkle, crab and lobster.

They used particular animal bones, horns and shells to fashion tools: needles, hole-punching awls, skin scrapers, points etc. They chipped flinty stones such as chert, jasper and felsite, to make arrow and spear heads and they used rocks for pounding grain and heating food. Some may have made pottery and grown crops in the summer: corn, beans and pumpkin, in small gardens.

Thus the Native Americans supplied their needs with the materials at hand, needing to trade very little. They ranged far if they wished to, traveling lightly and easily through the lake, forest and shore country that they understood. But usually they stayed in the home river basin that formed the territory of each group. They had strong rules against using too much of anything: taking too many fish, killing too many moose, cutting live trees, digging too many clams, so there would always be more for the next year, and for their children and grand children.

Colonial - (Pre-industrial - around 1800)

The first European settlers did not come to live in this part of Maine till the late 1700's. They were English-speaking and mostly from Massachusetts, which had been settled some 150 years earlier. Since the early 1500's, European fisherman had made camps on some of the further islands (Monhegan, Damariscove.) to salt and dry their catch before taking it back to Europe. French explorers, fur traders and missionaries had considerable contact with the Abenaqui on the coast but never made settlements near here. Agents of the British Navy landed to mark, cut and take the largest pine trees to make masts for their ships.

to mark a mast tree

"Kings Broad Arrow" for the British Navy

When the first settlers arrived on the "Maine" land in Camden and Rockport in 1768-69, there were few Abenaki

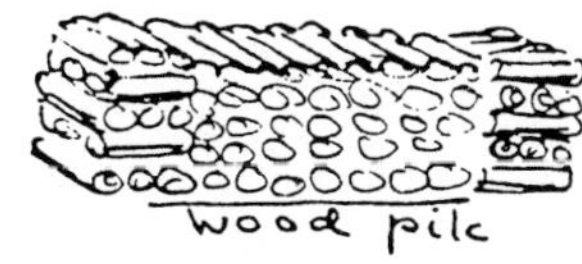

birch broom

living here. They had been attacked by plagues brought by earlier Europeans. Their social system was disrupted by the new tools (metal knives and guns) that they received from the Europeans and by alcohol which changed their behaviour. They had been killed by Europeans and they had fought with other native groups - the Abenaki against the "Etchemin" (Passamaquoddy + Malecite) and the "Tarratines" (Mic Mac). There were only a few families left when the first settlers came.

maul

hay fork

The Europeans who came here used many of the same resources that the Abenaki did: the clean water and air, the plants and animals of the woods, rivers and shore. But they used more of these resources, for they had no restraints built into their culture and laws. The settlers dug clams, hunted moose and bear, just like the Abenaki. But they killed many more of them every year. They were amazed by the amount of game and the huge trees when they first arrived, but the "game" was soon depleted and the clearing of the land begun.

mallet

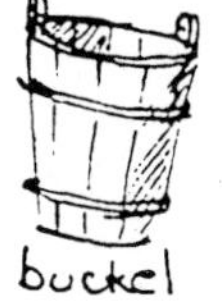

dipper

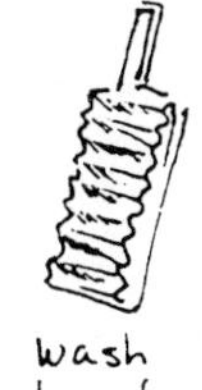

The wood from the forests was used to build cabins and boats. It was burned for fuel to cook and warm the cabins, and to make charcoal for iron work. These people worked iron into tools and that took a lot of fuel. They made utensils, furniture and containers largely out of wood, cutting it with iron tools. Still, iron was scarce and they used very little of it compared to later years.

scoop

Much of the wood was sold, shipped south to cities

churn

chair

① "The number of bear killed in Camden by Mr. Richards amounted to 30 and the number of moose to 70." account of the 1780's in Locke's "History of Camden"

charcoal mound

used up lots of wood

Some Uses of Wood

boat

CULTURE

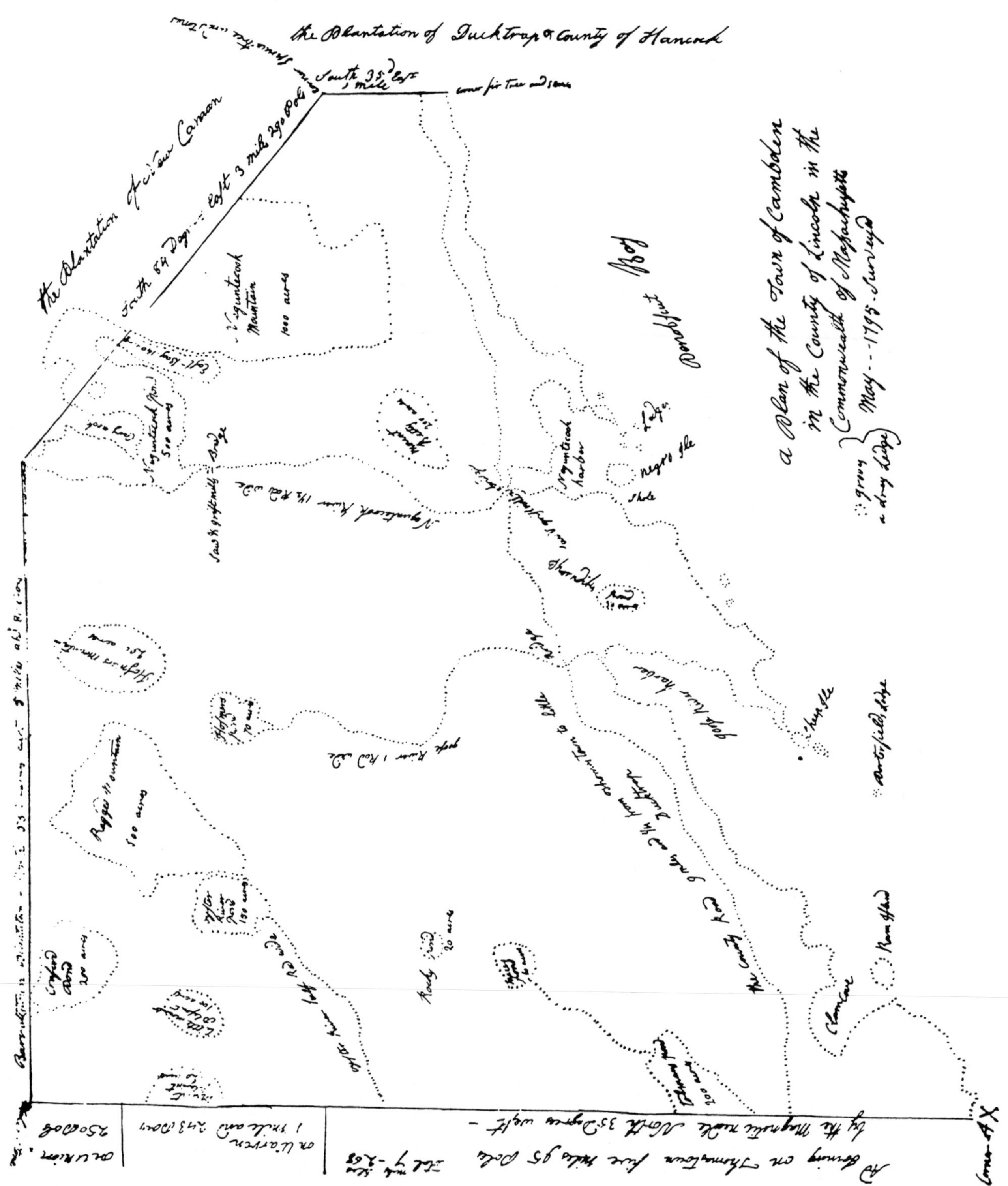

"a plan of the Town of Camden in the County of Lincoln in the Commonwealth of Massachusetts - May 1795. surveyed."

New Animals

and to the West Indies, and to Europe. After several decades most of the coastal forests were gone and, with them, the animals that lived from them. In their place were hayfields, pastures for cows and sheep, and fields for wheat, barley, oats, flax and, of course, Indian corn.

Stones were used to build foundations, to grind corn and piled into walls to mark the property boundaries.

The coastal settlers fished a great deal, and gathered shellfish and crustaceans. They used weirs to trap fish as the Abenaki did (and as their European ancestors had). Their clothing was partly of skins, but the skins were usually turned to leather by a tanning process using hemlock bark. They traded for woven cloth from the south until they began spinning and weaving their own wool and flax into cloth. They did not gather many plants, nor as many kinds of plants as the Abenaki had. They used berries and spring greens but did not bother with the roots and small nuts of the area. Instead they used the soil, to grow their own vegetables: European cabbage, carrots, turnips, lettuce, potatoes and the native crops of corn, pumpkin and beans. They planted fruit trees near their houses. They did not depend so much on wild game but kept their own chickens, pigs and cows.

They were most different from the Abenaki in their forms of transportation and use of energy. They used the water to travel by boat, far along the coast and to other countries. Great sailing vessels that harnessed the wind came to load lumber and bring settlers. The settlers used primitive dugouts and then plank rowing boats at first, but soon they began building

Plaintain "whitemans foot-steps (a weed

New Plants

Wheat

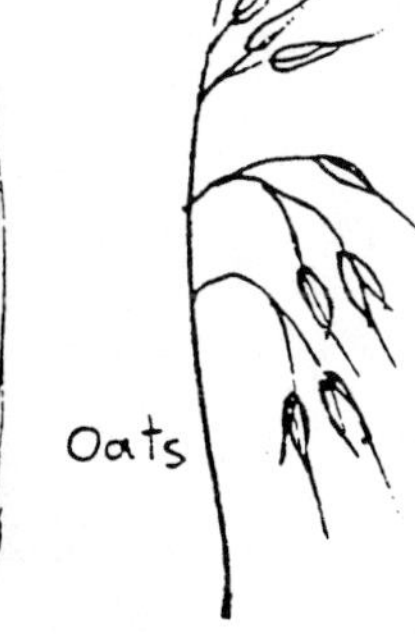

New Plants

Oats

blue

Flax

Apple

Lettuce

Cabbage

sail boats for themselves, to carry and sell wood, and for fishing.

On land, they walked on narrow trails at first, (see map) but soon they had oxen to pull sledges loaded with lumber and stones, and then carts widened the trails with increased traffic. Quite early, in 1806, permission was given to build a "turnpike" (Route 52) from Camden to what is now Lincolnville - along the edge of the lake.

They built mills on the little rivers: Megunticook, Goose River, Oyster River and Mill River (see Watershed map). Around these mill sites, tiny towns sprang up. By 1800 there were 15 small houses in the village of Camden. Altogether, about 900 people lived at the time in the whole town of Camden, which then included Rockport. The settlers built more mills up Megunticook until there were between nine and thirteen mill sites by the 1850's. The anadromous fish could no longer move up the streams to spawn and they largely disappeared from the area. Only the eels still wriggled up to spend their adult lives inland.

For all their use of water, wind and draft animals, these early settlers still lived largely by the strength of their own muscle. They used the energy from the food they raised and gathered here. They traded wood for some tools, utensils and clothing, but most of the materials they used came from the land around them. They lived from the land as the Abenaki had done, but in a different way

Industrial. (mid. 1800's to 1930's?)

By the mid. 19th century, things had changed dramatically in Camden and Rockport. About 5000 people lived in the town (from Camden to Glen Cove). This is about the same number of people we have had living here until quite recently. Settlements around the mill sites had grown

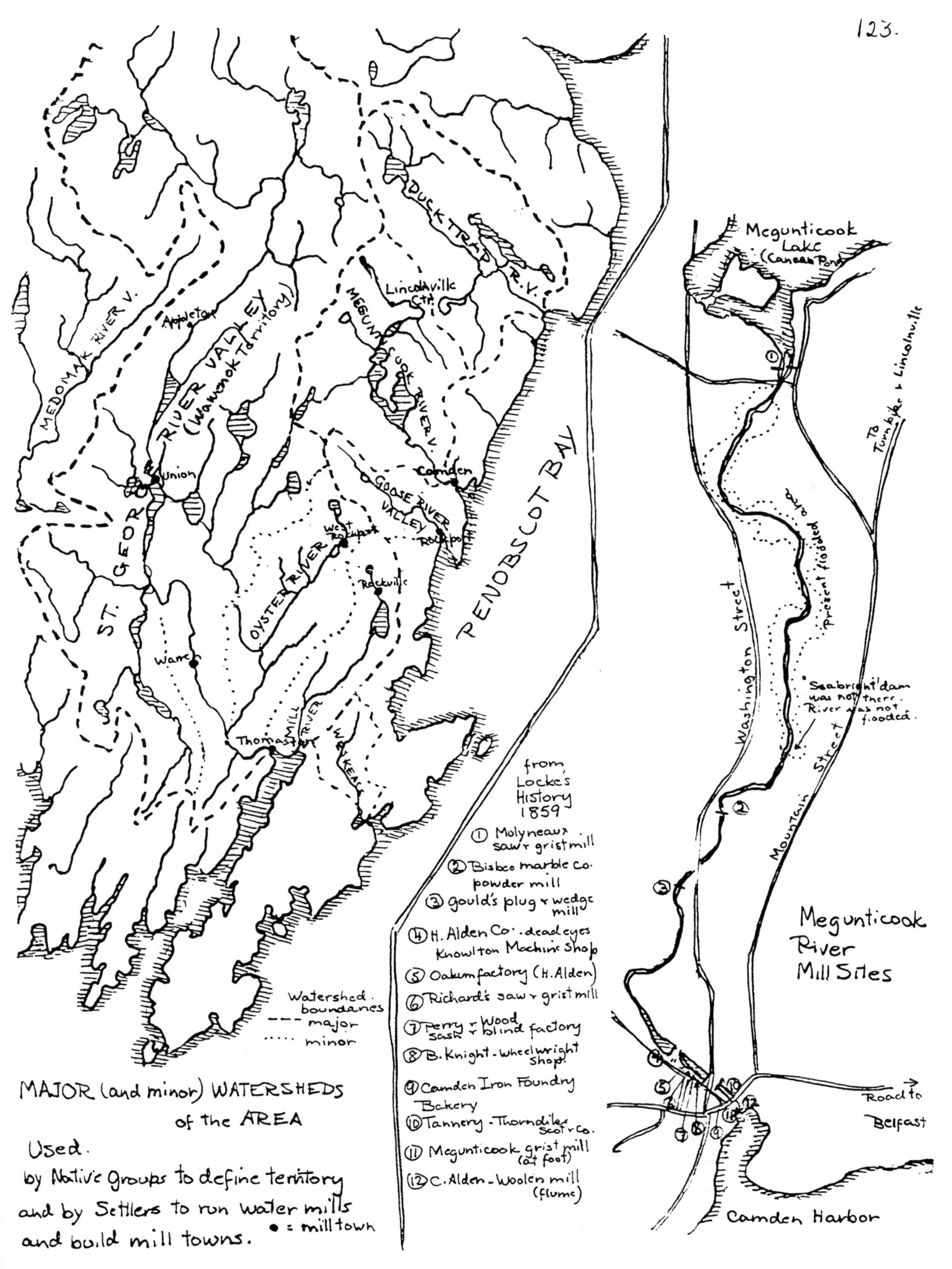
MEDOMAK RIVER V.
Appleton
RIVER VALLEY
(Wawenok Territory)
Union
GEOR
ST.
Warren
Thomaston
MILL RIVER
OYSTER RIVER
West Rockport
Rockville
Rockport
GOOSE RIVER VALLEY
Camden
MEGUNTICOOK RIVER V.
Lincolnville Ctr.
DUCKTRAP R.V.
PENOBSCOT BAY
Watershed boundaries
- - - major
. . . . minor
MAJOR (and minor) WATERSHEDS of the AREA
Used.
by Native Groups to define territory
and by Settlers to run water mills
and build mill towns.
• = mill town
from, Locke's History 1859
① Molyneaux saw & grist mill
② Bisbee marble co. powder mill
③ gould's plug & wedge mill
④ H. Alden Co. dead eyes Knowlton Machine Shop
⑤ Oakum factory (H. Alden)
⑥ Richard's saw & grist mill
⑦ Perry & Wood sash & blind factory
⑧ B. Knight - wheelwright shop.
⑨ Camden Iron Foundry Bakery
⑩ Tannery - Thorndike Scott & Co.
⑪ Megunticook grist mill (at foot)
⑫ C. Alden - Woolen mill (flume)
Megunticook Lake (Canaan Pond)
To Turnpike & Lincolnville
Present flooded area
Seabright dam was not there. River was not flooded.
Washington Street
Mountain Street
Megunticook River Mill Sites
Road to Belfast
Camden Harbor

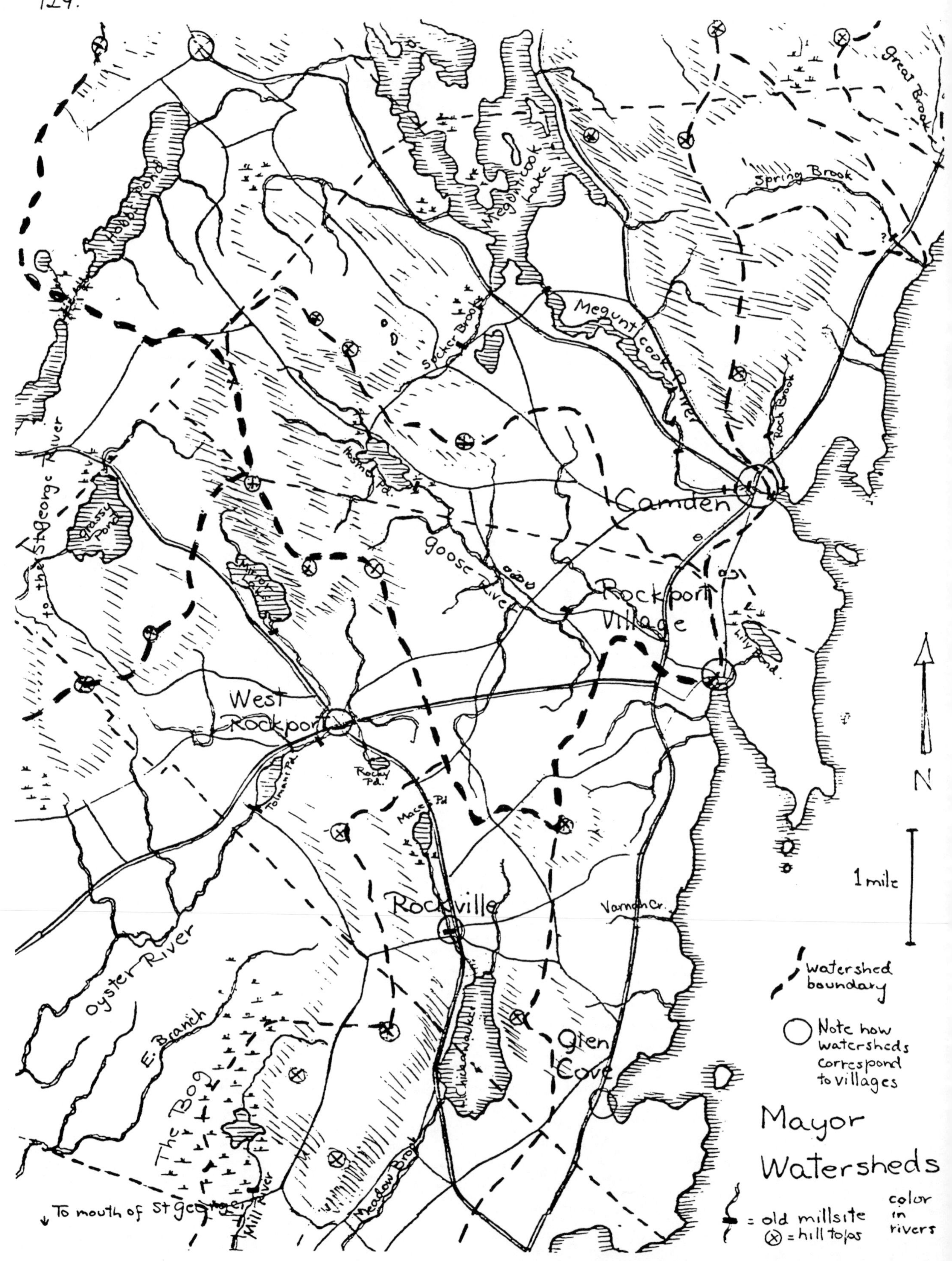

Great Brook
Spring Brook
Megunticook Lake
Megunticook River
Sucker Brook
Hosmer Pd.
Rock Brook
Camden
to the St George River
Grassy Pond
Mirror Lake
Goose River
Rockport Village
Lily Pond
West Rockport
Rocky Pd.
Tolman Pd.
Mace's Pd.
Rockville
Varnum Cr.
Oyster River
E. Branch
The Bog
Chickawaukie
Glen Cove
Mill River
Meadow Brook
To mouth of St George R.
N
1 mile
watershed boundary
Note how watersheds correspond to villages
Mayor Watersheds
= old millsite
= hill tops
color in rivers

larger, with Camden on the Megunticook being the busiest. In Camden, in addition to the usual grist mill, saw mill and boat building shops, there were mills producing sashes and blinds, plugs and dead eyes, oakum, a bark mill and tannery, woolen mills, a wheelwright shop and an iron foundry and a powder mill. On Spring Brook, there was a stave and shingle mill. Goose River, as Rockport was called, had a grist mill, saw mill, stave mill and lime kilns.

for the grist mill

All these little factories were hooked up to the water power of the small but strong rivers of the area. and the communities clustered around them. The people who lived here were attached to the river systems but in a different way from the Abenaki, who had used them for travel and fishing.

for the sawmill

The fields were cleared for miles around, though there was still timber on the mountains. On this land, hay, grain, sheep and cattle were still raised, though the soil had not proved as fertile under European methods of agriculture as the first settlers had hoped. (Many of the early farmers had left for the Middle West when Ohio opened up in 1815.)① The farmers of the area still lived more like the early settlers than the towns people did, but they raised less of their food and bought more tools. They still built their houses and barns out of local lumber. The hunting was not very good, the rivers were not passable to fish and they now carried the wastes of the barkmills, tannery and woolen washing. But the clams were still good to dig and there were fish to be had in the bay.

window sashes

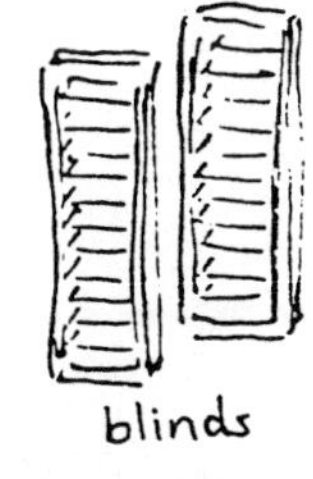
blinds

The people of the region now specialized: some in growing food, like apples, some in fishing, some in shipbuilding, both for the region and for outsiders. Others worked in or managed the small factories, producing

barrel stave barrel

from the wheelwright

① in 1816, there was a killing summer frost -(following the explosion of a volcano in the Pacific)- The crop damage was such that many New Englanders left in the following years.

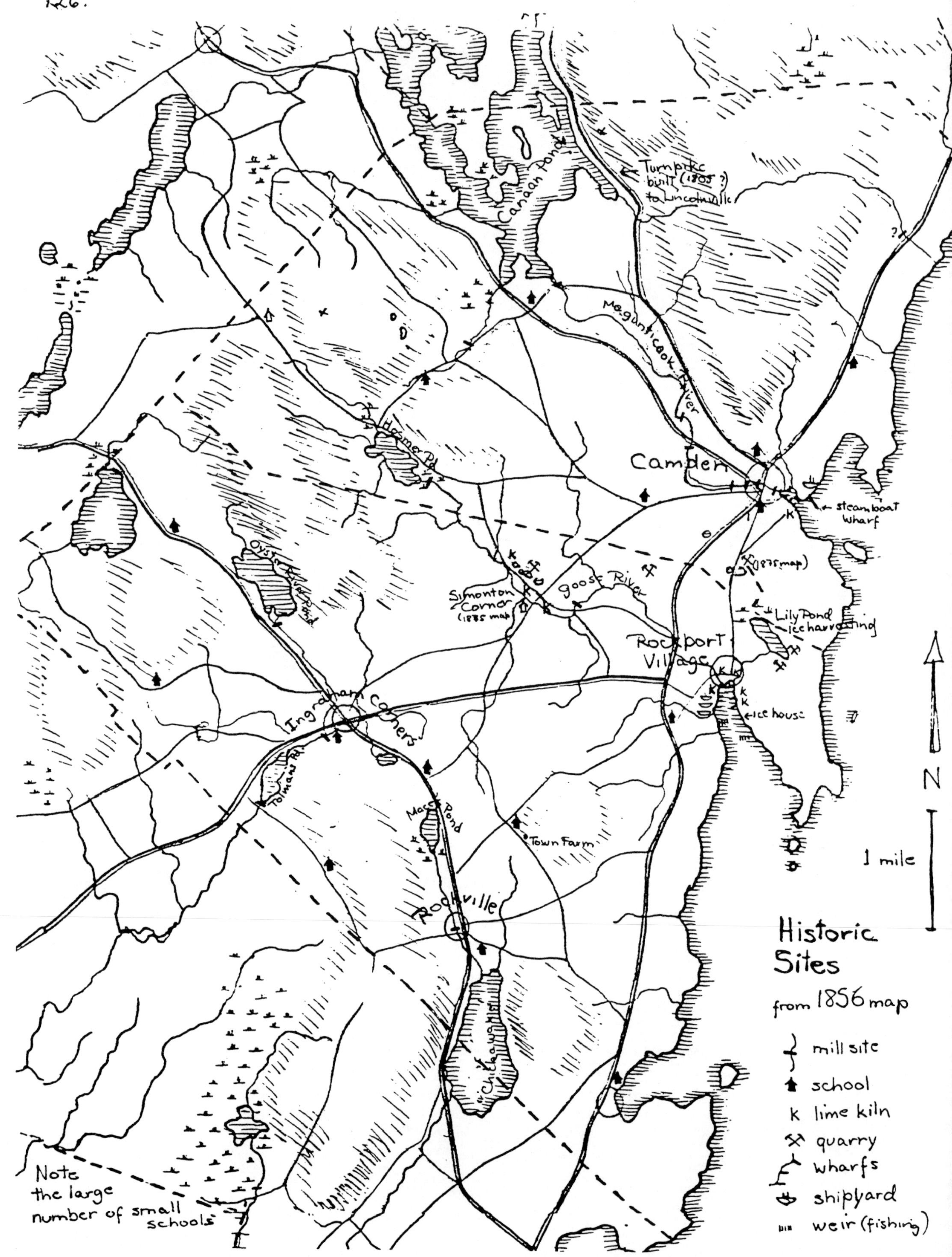

Turnpike built (1805 ?) to Lincolnville
Canaan Pond
Megunticook River
Hosmer Pd.
Camden
steamboat wharf
Oyster River Pond
Simonton Corner (1885 map)
Goose River
(1875 map)
Lily Pond ice harvesting
Rockport Village
ice house
Ingraham Corners
Tolman Rd.
Mace's Pond
Town Farm
Rockville
Chickawaukie
N
1 mile
Historic Sites from 1856 map
mill site
school
k lime kiln
quarry
wharfs
shipyard
weir (fishing)
Note the large number of small schools

things that were largely sold and used outside the region itself. People now bought, if they could afford it, cloth for clothing and ready-made clothes. Their shoes were usually from somewhere else. They bought dishes and cooking utensils made in other regions, even other countries. Some of their food already came from the Middle West. All kinds of tools and ingenious machines were traded for the money made from the town's products.

Many of the products of the region were made from wood that grew here: the ships, the barrel staves, furniture, shingles, bark for tanning. The wool could be produced locally. Another product that was exported by the region was lime, for use as cement in building. It was made from the limestone (actually a dolomite marble) mined in the quarry we now use as a dump, and from the quarries at Simonton's Corner. The stone was "cooked" in kilns in Rockport and Camden, using wood brought in on boats. The "quick" lime was shipped out in locally made barrels. Even the ponds were "mined" in the late 19th century. Ice was cut in the Lily Pond, stored in ice houses and shipped to warm southern ports to cool iceboxes. And the ships of Camden and Rockport made the fortunes of famous sea captains who traded all over the world.

The richer townspeople really belonged to a much larger region than Camden and Rockport. They were connected, through their trade and travel, to other cities on the East coast, to the Midwest, to the West Indies, to Europe and to the Far East. They had better roads, horses and carriages, and, eventually, horseless carriages. There was a telegraph system from the 1850's and even a horseless trolley from Thomaston to Camden (1900 to 1930).

The people with less money still lived largely on the land, hunting, gathering some plant food

Ice cutting

Old Lime Kilns, Rockport

CAMDEN and ROCKPORT 1864

Cleared & Wooded Land.

Contrast this map with a modern version. Which has more forest?

::: orchards

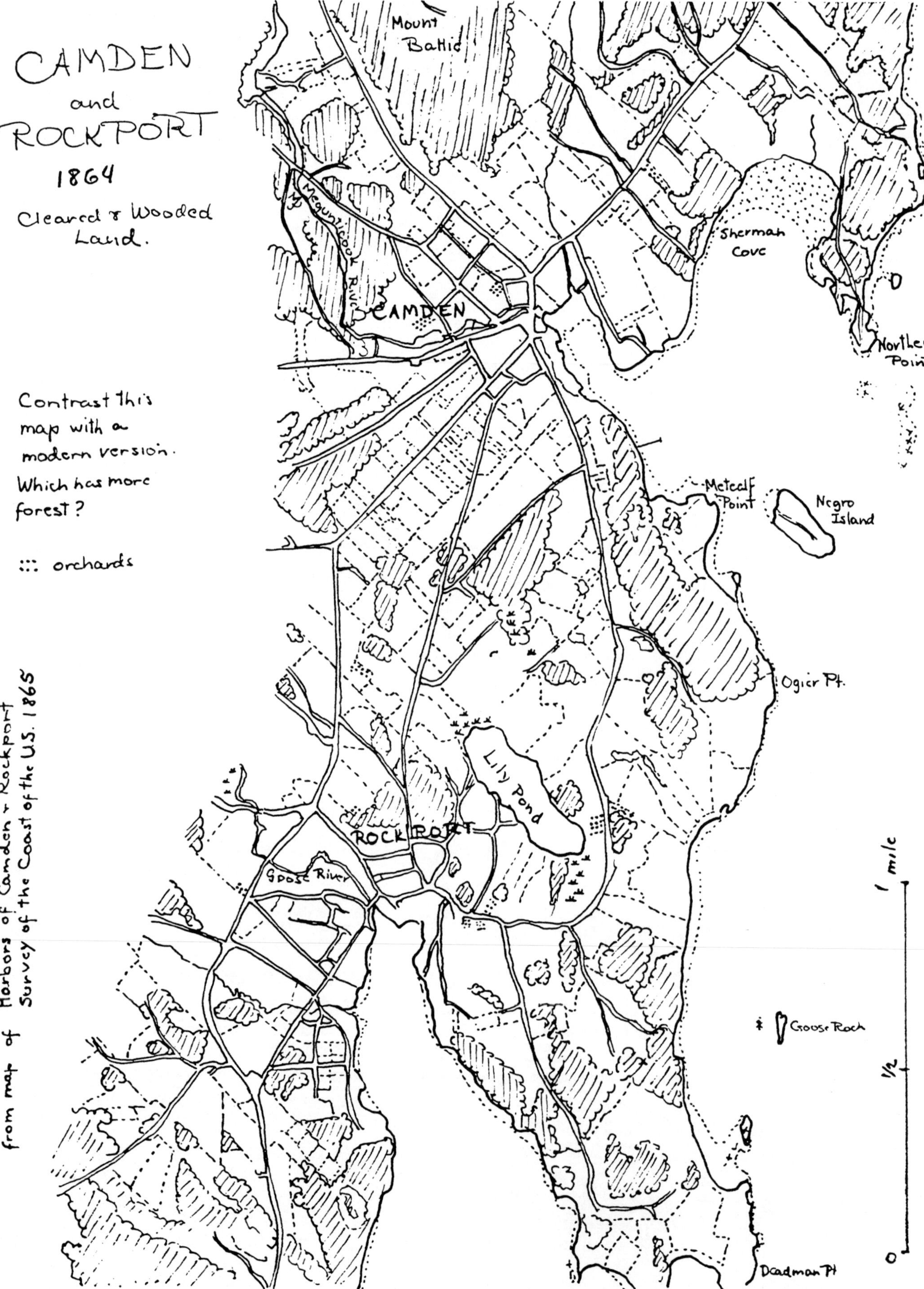

from map of Harbors of Camden & Rockport
Survey of the Coast of the U.S. 1865

HUMAN SEASONAL CYCLE in C.-R.

–1770 Abenaki Hunting & Gathering	1800 Settlers - Agricultural	1850–1900 ... Industrial	1980 NOW	
pop. 20-100 (guess)	pop. about 1000	pop. about 4,000	pop. 6,000 (-15,000 summ	
HARD TIMES MOON ○ mending gear; winter games	SCHOOL; cutting wood; stone hauling; shingle & nail making	sliding; skating; sleigh rides	ski-ing; unemployment; Retired people go South for winter; SCHOOL	Jan
CRUST OF SNOW MOON ○ Great Hunt: moose, caribou, otter, beaver, bear (deer)	lambing; pruning		ice fishing	Feb
EGG LAYING(?) MOON ○ ice fishing; smelt fishing; maple sap	calves; Town Meeting		maple syrup	Mar
SPRING FISH MOON ○ make canoe with spring bark; Canada goose; waterfowl eggs	Ice out		Easter	April
sturgeon - salmon; herring - shad; alewife				
PLANTING MOON; root & bulb digging	hauling manure; stump pulling; Plant potatoes, wheat, flax; Plant corn, beans		working on boats	May
SEALS RISE MOON ○	washing sheep; shearing			
corn & pumpkin planting; clams; lobsters; mussels; MOVE TO COAST & ISLANDS	weeding; bee swarms		Mowing lawns	June
RIPE BERRY MOON ○	mowing; pulling flax	swimming; Fourth of July		
Blueberries; seal & black-fish	Haying; blueberries	hayrides	blueberries; Sailing; Angling	July
SEALS FATTENING MOON ○ raspberries; hunting	Haying; raspberries		House painting; Summer People & Tourists	Aug
blackberries; cod	Harvesting; blackberries		Summer work: restaurants, shops, motels, schooners	
MOOSE CALLING MOON ○ eels (in weir)	threshing grain; winnowing	canning		Sep
still hunting by canoe at night; move back inland			SCHOOL	
FAT TAME ANIMALS MOON ○ harvest corn & pumpkin; dry & cache food	gather apples; cider making; husk corn		apples	
salmon go up river	hauling dung; stone digging		hunting game birds; Halloween	Oct
WATER FISH MOON ○ hunt caribou, moose & beaver	steer & hog killing; root cellaring	deer hunting		Nov
		Thanksgiving		
BIG MOON ○ return to villages; mending & work with skins, cordage etc	SCHOOL	New Years & Christmas		Dec

like the people before them, growing some food, building with the materials at hand, wood and stone, and still using their muscles to make their living. Meanwhile, the "money making" resources of the region began to give out. Lumber had to be brought from farther and farther away. When coal replaced wood as a fuel, the local lime kilns lost their advantage and the industry died. Wooden ships were replaced by metal ones built elsewhere (except for the wooden hulled mine sweepers built here in WWII). Electric refrigerators replaced ice boxes, so the ice industry stopped. The towns became poorer. Toward the end of the century, people began to come here from the southern cities to "use" the scenery and the cool summer air, just as the Abenaki once came down to the coast in the summer to fish and escape the blackflies and mosquitos. This is a new way of "trading" the region's resources.

The Late 1900's, now.

Now, 100 years later, the people of Camden and Rockport depend even less on the resources of the region. Most of us belong to an enormous "region" that encompasses most of the earth. Very little of our food, clothing or shelter originates here. Our "goods" are mostly from far away.

The land which was used to grow food in the 1900's has grown up into woods again and many of the plants and animals have come back. Our food now comes from the Middle West, from California, Florida and Central America. Our household goods and clothing come largely from Eastern Asia and the South where people work for very low wages. Some of the materials for building our houses (sand, gravel, shingles, some lumber) come rom nearby. The ways that people used to get their food and goods are now considered hobbies, or sports, or something that only the unemployed have time for. Except for lobstering, a few chicken farms and apple orchards, people are not making a living in hunting, gathering or agriculture

Plant Cover
and
Land Use
(1977)
from
Maine
Coastal
Inventory
CAMDEN
ROCKPORT
CKLAND
Megunticook Lake
Hosmer Pond
Mirror Lake
Chickawaukie Pond
Camden Harbor
Curtis I.
Deadman Pt.
(color in forests with greens)
U = Urban Area
† = Cemetary
Q = Quarry
SD = Sanitary Dump
AD = Autodump
GC = Golf Course
Ba = Exposed ledge
= Powerline
S = Softwood
H = Hardwood
M = Mixed wood
A = Agricultural
B = Blueberries
F = Other fields
O = Orchard
W = Wetlands
= Alders
SC = Scrub
(from Aereal photographs)

here at the moment.

To buy the things we need, we trade our labor. We work in the tannery or the Woolen mill⊚, or in small boat building yards, just as we did 100 years ago. But we also make tiny electronic devices and lightweight tents. We publish magazines and books. The materials we use in these industries come from far away; even the wool, and the hides for the tannery are mostly from outside the country. We work for the summer people, sailors and boat owners, tourists and retired people. Some of us are craftspeople and artists, and our works are sold far away. Some of us commute to far cities to make money to live here.

Our transportation is almost entirely by automobile and truck, using gasoline energy that comes from far away. We have fairly good roads, but no trolley or railway, because we have all been able to afford cars and gasoline. We no longer use the water power of the rivers or the force of the wind, except for recreation in sailboats. We don't use water for transportation of goods or people. We use engines and motors run by oil or the electricity from oil or nuclear power to do most of our work.* We rarely use hand tools of the sort the early settlers had. We no longer use the force of our muscles or the muscles of domestic animals for work.

In some ways, we resemble the early settlers more than our parents did. We are using more wood now to heat our houses. We must take care of this renewable resource and not cut the forest faster than it can grow. Some of us are beginning to produce more of our own food as energy prices increase. and food from far away costs more. We resemble the Abenaki more in that we are trying to control our use of resources - i.e. we try not to hunt too many deer or take lobster that are too small. We are learning to keep our water clean. We are thinking about limiting our wood cutting by good woodlot management. We have set land aside as forest in the State Park. In the future, good land may be protected for agricultural use.

* One sixth of our electricity is produced by water power (1984) ⊚-converted to synthetic felts (1982)

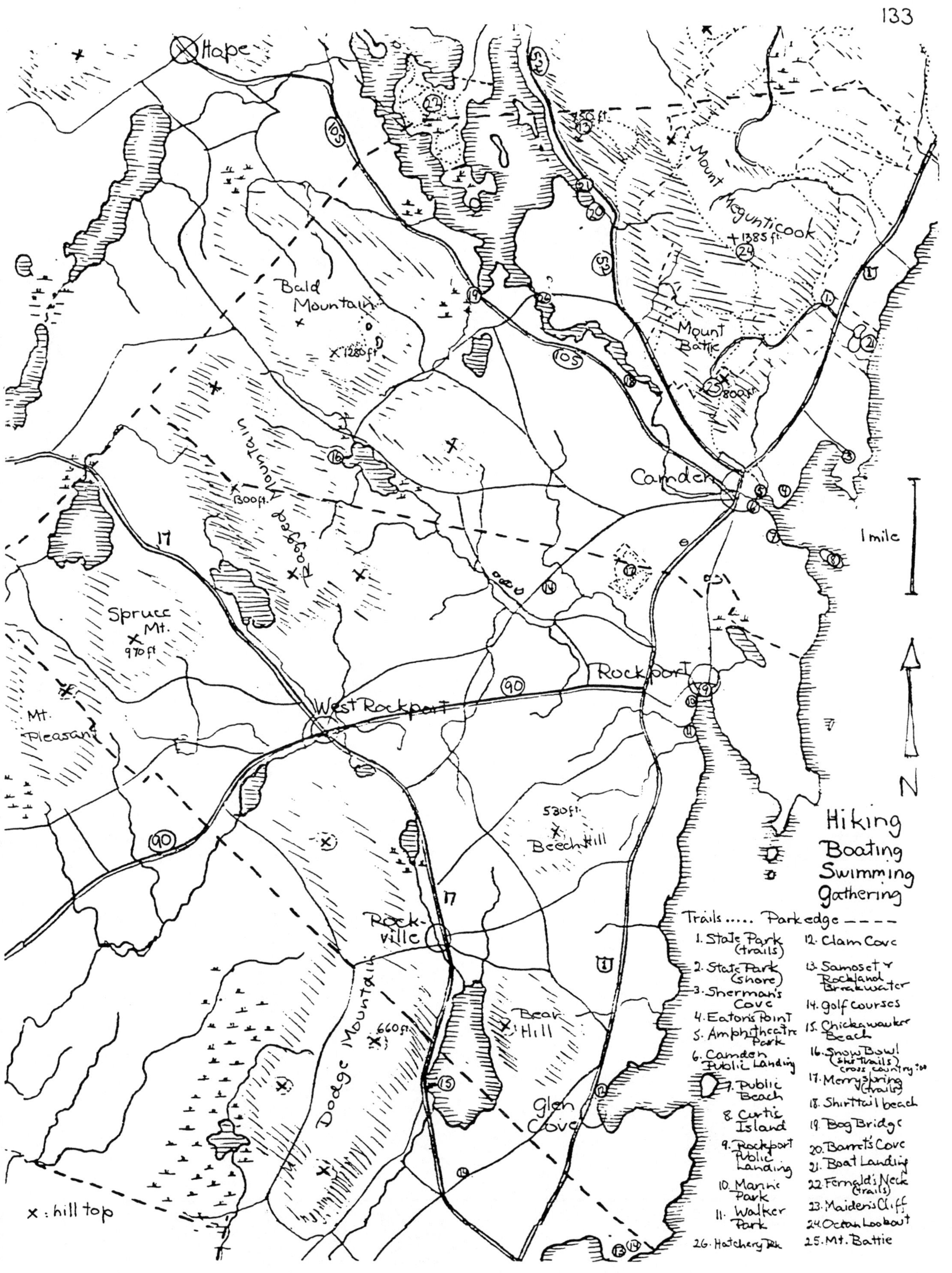
Hope
Mount
Megunticook
1385 ft.
Bald
Mountain
1280 ft
Mount
Battie
800 ft
Camden
Ragged Mountain
1300 ft.
17
Spruce
Mt.
970 ft
Mt.
Pleasant
West Rockport
90
Rockport
1 mile
N
530 ft.
Beech Hill
Hiking
Boating
Swimming
Gathering
Rock-
ville
Bear
Hill
Dodge Mountain
660 ft.
Glen
Cove
105
x : hill top
Trails..... Park edge ----
1. State Park (trails)
2. State Park (shore)
3. Sherman's Cove
4. Eaton's Point
5. Amphitheatre Park
6. Camden Public Landing
7. Public Beach
8. Curtis Island
9. Rockport Public Landing
10. Marine Park
11. Walker Park
12. Clam Cove
13. Samoset & Rockland Breakwater
14. Golf courses
15. Chickawaukee Beach
16. Snow Bowl (ski trails) cross country too
17. Merryspring (trails)
18. Shirttail beach
19. Bog Bridge
20. Barrett's Cove
21. Boat Landing
22. Fernald's Neck (trails)
23. Maiden's Cliff
24. Ocean Lookout
25. Mt. Battie
26. Hatchery Pk

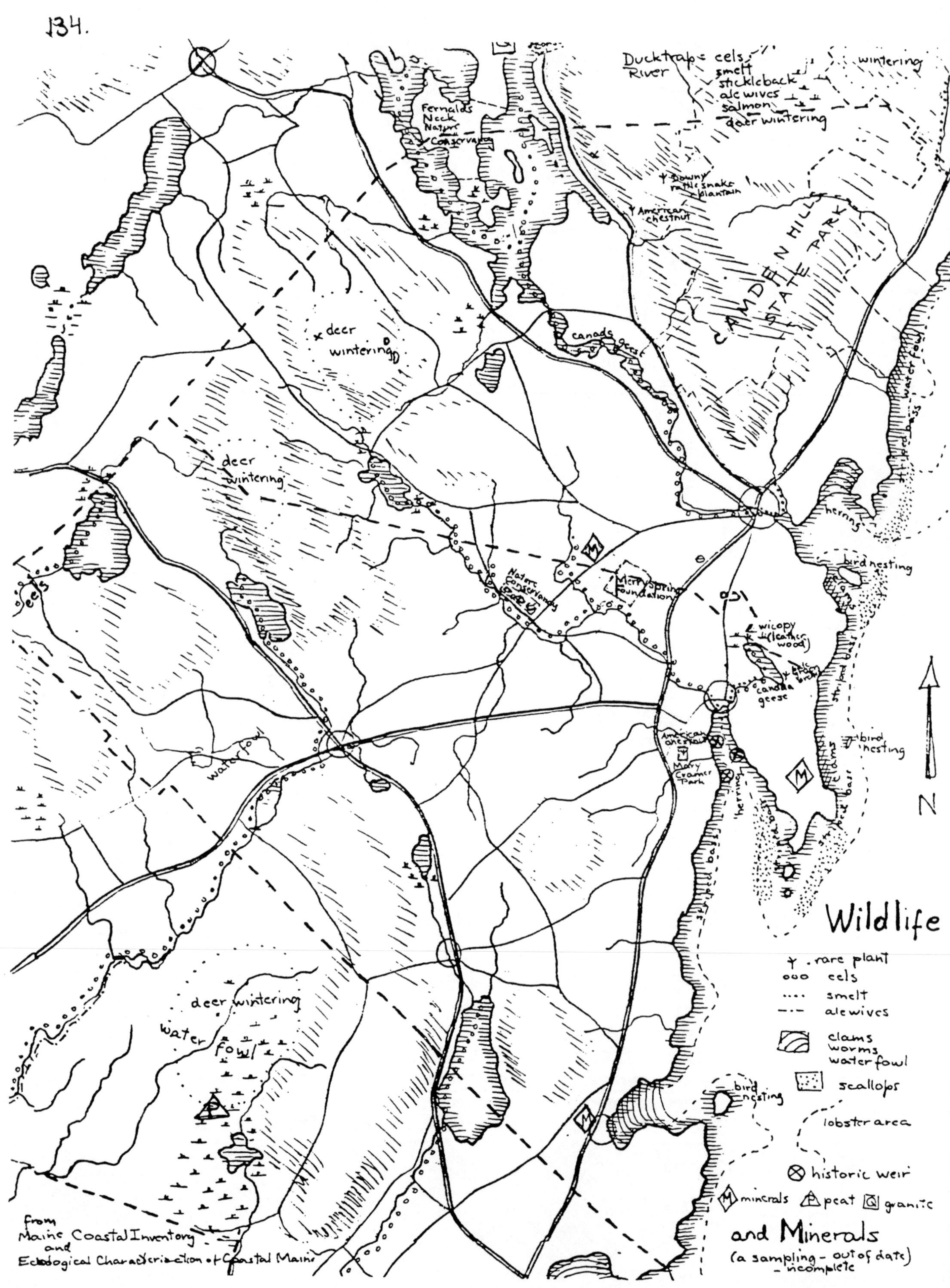
Ducktrap River
eels
smelt
stickleback
alewives
salmon
deer wintering
wintering
Fernalds Neck Nature Conservancy
Downy rattlesnake plantain
American chestnut
CAMDEN HILLS STATE PARK
deer wintering
canada geese
waterfowl
striped bass
deer wintering
herring
bird nesting
Merryspring Foundation
Nature Conservancy
wicopy (leatherwood)
canada geese
eels
waterfowl
American chestnut
Mary Cramer Park
herring
striped bass
clams
bird nesting
N
Wildlife
rare plant
eels
smelt
alewives
clams
worms
waterfowl
scallops
lobster area
historic weir
minerals
peat
granite
and Minerals
(a sampling - out of date)
- incomplete
deer wintering
water fowl
bird nesting
from
Maine Coastal Inventory
and
Ecological Characterization of Coastal Maine

We still need to use the water and air of the region. We must guard our water supplies by maintaining forested watersheds and by protecting the aquifers from pollution. We must be sensitive to the quality of air that is threatened by car and truck exhausts, careless woodburning and by air systems moving east from more industrial regions, carrying acid rain.

We already use our wood. We may need our soil in the future and must protect it from erosion and compaction. We have changed our environment considerably already, by building houses and roads, damming rivers and allowing wastes to flow into water, air and soil. What changes will we make in our environment in the years to come? Will we be able to make a living in this land in the future and in what ways will we do so?

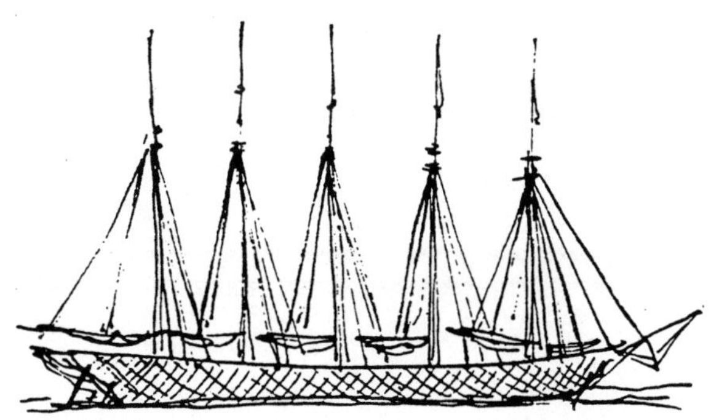

Five masted schooner

1999 Update:

Bear have come back, and coyote have moved in. Many new houses and their roads have been built into the woods, on the hills and the water's edge. The car and truck population has risen sharply and strip development is growing. The offshore fisheries have collapsed; elvers are being netted aggressively in the spring; lobstering is still strong. The dump now recycles and the leachate is pumped to the sewage plant.

this page maybe cut into 3 sections + assembled into a complete panoramic view.

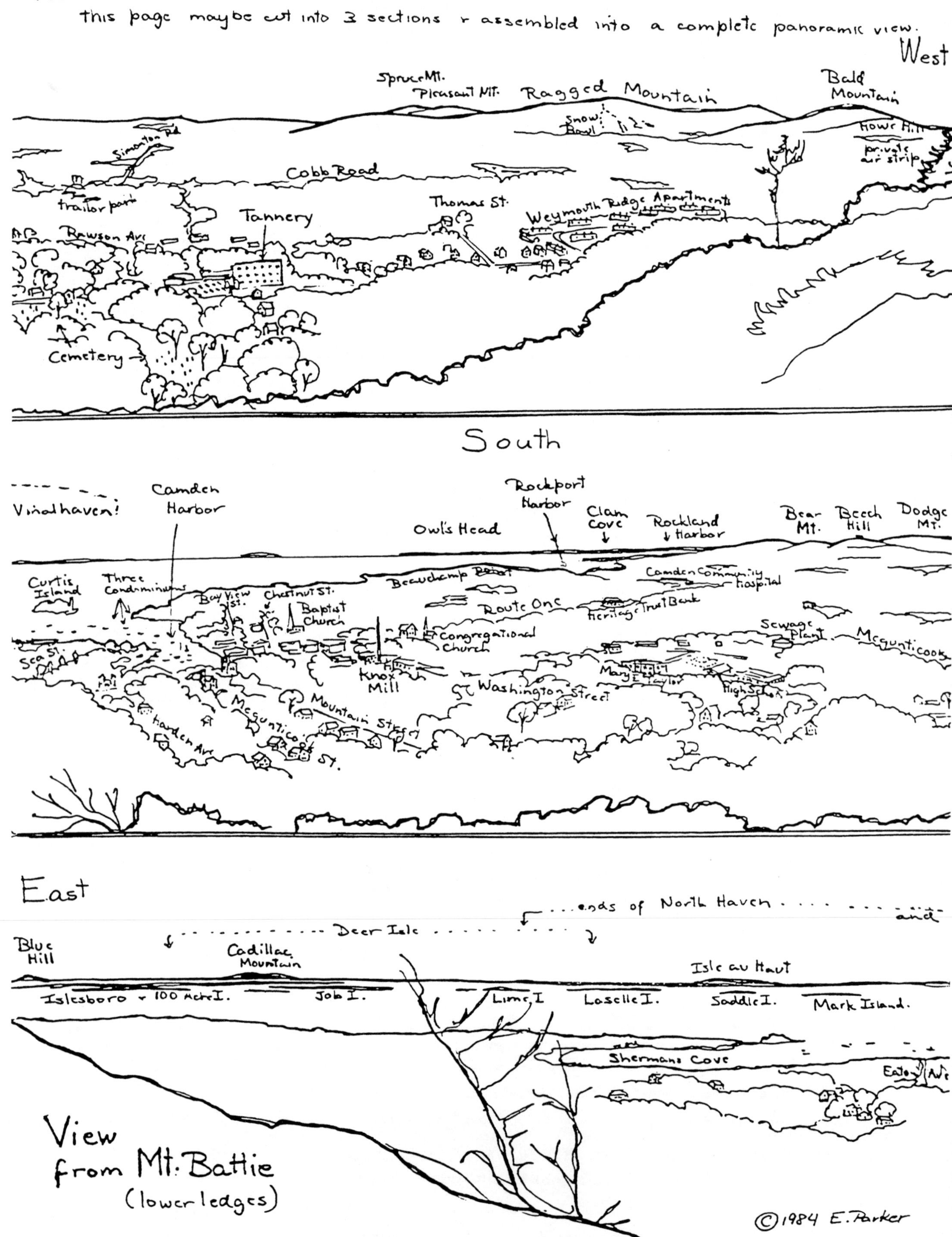

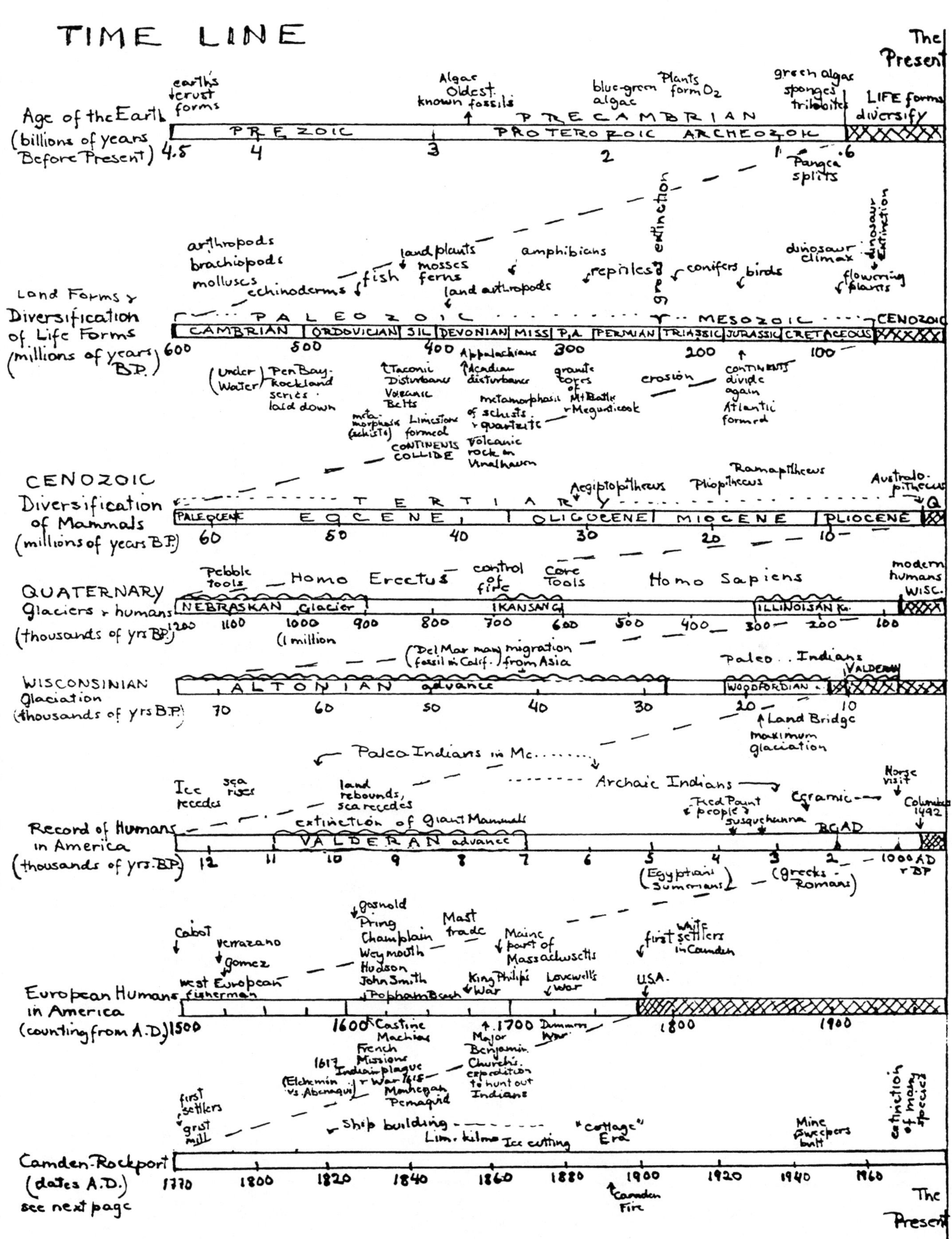
TIME LINE
The Present
Age of the Earth (billions of years Before Present)
earth's crust forms
Algae Oldest known fossils
blue-green algae
Plants form O2
green algae sponges trilobites
LIFE forms diversify
PRECAMBRIAN
PREZOIC
PROTEROZOIC
ARCHEOZOIC
4.5
4
3
2
1
.6
Pangea splits
Land Forms & Diversification of Life Forms (millions of years B.P.)
arthropods
brachiopods
molluscs
echinoderms
fish
land plants
mosses
ferns
land arthropods
amphibians
reptiles
great extinction
conifers
birds
dinosaur climax
dinosaur extinction
flowering plants
PALEOZOIC
MESOZOIC
CENOZOIC
CAMBRIAN
ORDOVICIAN
SIL
DEVONIAN
MISS
P.A.
PERMIAN
TRIASSIC
JURASSIC
CRETACEOUS
600
500
400
300
200
100
(Under Water)
Pen Bay-Rockland series laid down
Taconic Disturbance
Volcanic Belts
meta-morphosis (schists)
Limestone formed
CONTINENTS COLLIDE
Appalachians
Acadian disturbance
metamorphosis of schists & quartzite
Volcanic rock on Vinalhaven
granite cores of Mt Battie & Megunticook
erosion
CONTINENTS divide again
Atlantic formed
CENOZOIC Diversification of Mammals (millions of years B.P.)
Aegiptopithecus
Pliopithecus
Ramapithecus
Australopithecus
TERTIARY
Q
PALEOCENE
EOCENE
OLIGOCENE
MIOCENE
PLIOCENE
60
50
40
30
20
10
QUATERNARY Glaciers & humans (thousands of yrs B.P.)
Pebble tools
Homo Erectus
control of fire
Core Tools
Homo Sapiens
modern humans
WISC.
NEBRASKAN Glacier
KANSAN G.
ILLINOISAN G.
1200
1100
1000
900
800
700
600
500
400
300
200
100
(1 million
(Del Mar man fossil in Calif.)
migration from Asia
Paleo . Indians
WISCONSINIAN Glaciation (thousands of yrs B.P.)
ALTONIAN advance
WOODFORDIAN
VALDERAN
70
60
50
40
30
20
10
Land Bridge
maximum glaciation
Paleo Indians in Me.
Archaic Indians
Norse visit
Ice recedes
sea rises
land rebounds, sea recedes
extinction of Giant Mammals
Fluted Point people
Susquehanna
Ceramic
Columbus 1492
BC AD
Record of Humans in America (thousands of yrs B.P.)
VALDERAN advance
12
11
10
9
8
7
6
5
4
3
2
1000 AD & BP
(Egyptians Sumerians)
(Greeks Romans)
Cabot
Verrazano
Gomez
west European fisherman
Gosnold
Pring
Champlain
Weymouth
Hudson
John Smith
Popham Beach
Mast trade
Maine part of Massachusetts
King Philip's War
Lovewell's War
first white settlers in Camden
USA.
European Humans in America (counting from A.D.)
1500
1600
1700
1800
1900
Castine Machias
French Missions
1617 Indian plague
& War 1615 (Etchemin vs. Abenaqui)
Monhegan Pemaquid
Major Benjamin Church's expedition to hunt out Indians
Dummer War
first settlers
grist mill
Ship building
Lime kilns
Ice cutting
"cottage" Era
Mine Sweepers built
extinction of many species
Camden-Rockport (dates A.D.) see next page
1770
1800
1820
1840
1860
1880
1900
1920
1940
1960
Camden Fire
The Present

The Last 200 years .Camden-Rockport

1768-69 First settlers

grist mills set up + saw mills

During Revolution "shaving mills" pirates scour coast

Peter Ott's Tavern (Bartel Rockpt.)

1780 May 19 "The Dark Day"

1791 Camden incorporated

1791 Maine becomes part of Mass.

1792 1st school set up.

1792 bridge over Megunticook R.

1796 17 houses in town -schooner built

1807 Conway House

1806 alewives can't get up Megunticook

1802 Turnpike Drive built to Lincolnville

1814 "Sailors War"

1814 .... shipbuilding .... 1848-60 Clippers .... big ship yards

1816 hard freeze in summer

"Ohio Fever" exodus to Mid West

1823 first steamboat visits

& Saltworks on Beauchamp Pt.

1825 papermill

Lime Kilns .... lime builds Back Bay + New York City ....

1834 steamboat 1932 service

1836 first bank

1837 Chestnut St Baptist Church

Mills on Megunticook: oakum, powder, grist woolen, anchors, tannery, shingles, plugs etc

Temperance movement

1847 doughnuts with holes in Rockpt.

telegraph arrives 1848-54

1850 Lighthouse on Curtis Island

1864 maiden falls off Maiden Cliff

Elm St School built 1868

summer boarders

bay freezes 1868 + 187

POPULATION .... 331 .... 872 .... 1607 .... 1828 P. .... 2200 P. .... 3000 P. .... 4000 P. .... 5000 P. .... 4,500 P.

POPULATION INCREASE

1770 | 1780 | 1790 | 1800 | 1810 | 1820 | 1830 | 1840 | 1850 | 1860 | 1870

---

wood runs out coal brought in for lime kilns

1892 - 1932 Trolley from Camden to Thomaston

1886-94 Limerock Railway - Rckpt.

Orchards established

Ice cutting .... on Lily Pond

1891 Rockport splits off

1891. Fire destroys downtown Camden 1892 - brick buildings replace

1896 Old High School built

1907 trotting Park behind H.S.

1904 Village shop opens

WWI 1917 ship building 13-4 masters

1928 Camden Library opens

Lime quarry closes

chicken houses start

1934 trailer truck destroys Rockport bridge

1932 steamer service to Portland finishes

WWII wooden mine sweepers built in Camden

"Peyton Place" 1957 filmed

& Camden Community Hospital moved to Elm St.

average summer population estimated at 15,000

1880 | 1890 | 1900 | 1910 | 1920 | 1930 | 1940 | 1950 | 1960 | 1970 | 1980 →

1878 Hurricane

Cottage Era .. 1886 Norumbega summer people

1887 Water Works - water from Mirror Lake

1887 Baptist Church spire removed

1891 Electricity

1892 Telephone

1897 .... summit House on Mt. Battie → (burns)

1907 Fire in Rockport Ice houses burn

1904-1905 bay freezes over

tower on Mt. Battie built

Music Colony in Rockport

1921 Spite House moved to Beauchamp Pt.

1930 Fire on Mt. Battie

1930's CCC work on Camden Hills State Park

1933 bay freezes

POPULATION INCREASE

People start moving up from South

1980 Old High School torn down

Baptist Church spire back up.

POPULATION .... 2,825 C. + 2,314 R. = 5,200 C. + R. .... 6000 C. + R. .... 6000 C. + R. .... 7,400 C. + R.

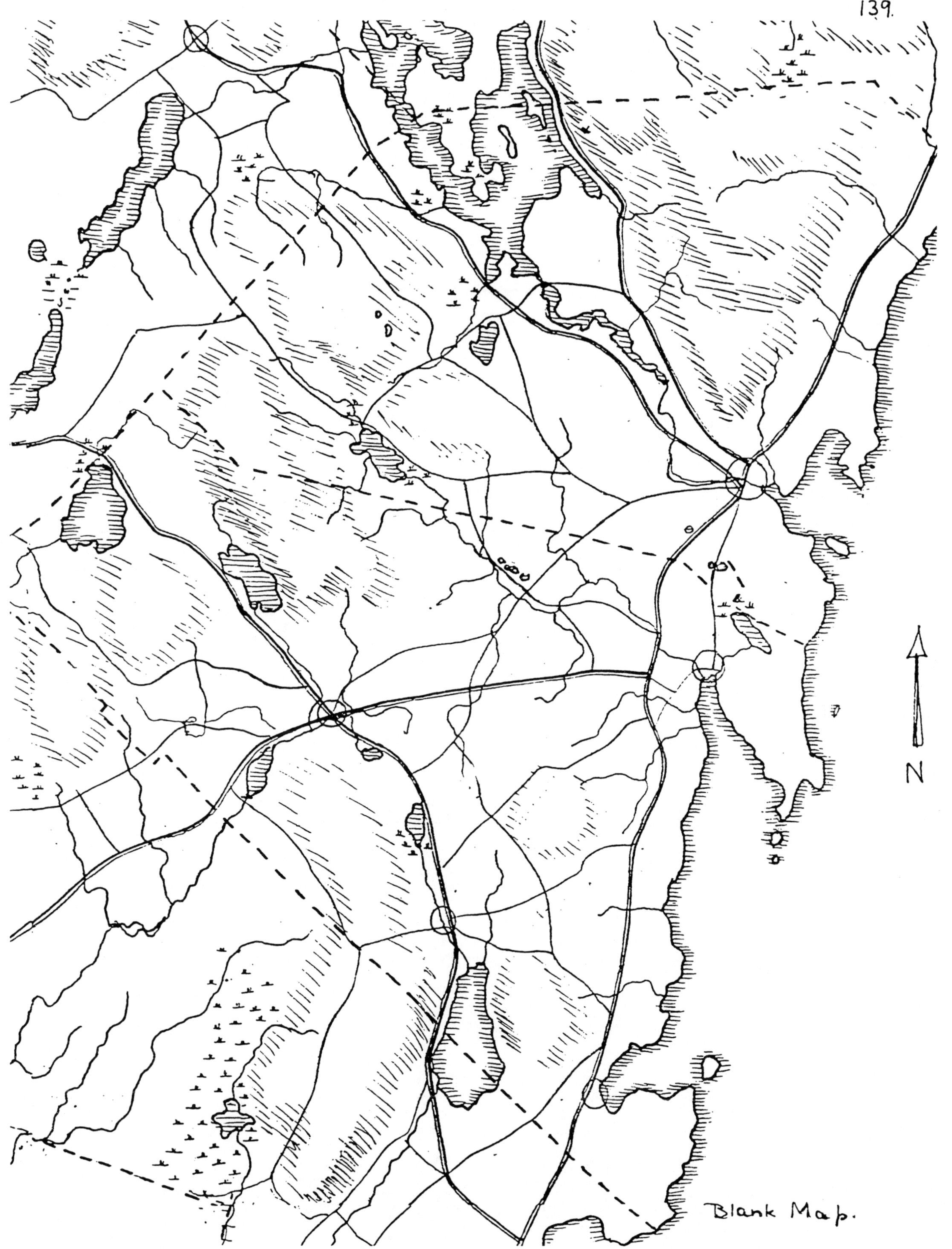
N
Blank Map.

BIBLIOGRAPHY & SOURCES

General

Bean, Richards, Hyland. - Checklist of Vascular Plants of Maine - Josselyn Bot. Soc. 1966

Buschbaum, R & M. - Basic Ecology - Boxwood Pr. 1957

Butcher, R.D. - Field Guide to Acadia National Park - Readers Digest Pr. 1977.

Camden Comprehensive Plan 1962

Campbell, Hyland, Campbell - Winterkeys to Woody Plants of Maine - UMO 1975

Ecological Characterization of Coastal Maine - Bio. Services Program. Fish & Wildlife Service U.S. Dept of Interior 1981 (available at town office & E. Midcoast Regional Plan)

Environmental Awareness - Coop. Extension Service of N.E. States. UMO (4-H teaching materials)

Fernald's Neck Preserve Inventory - The Nature Conservancy - 20 Federal St. Brunswick Me. see also guide booklet by Maine Reach School, Chewonki Foundation

Golden Guides - Golden Press - titles: Mammals, Fishes, Seashores, Pond life. Acadia National Park. North American Indian Arts, Insects, Weeds Insect Pests, Trees, Non-Flowering Plants, Reptiles & Amphibians, Rocks and Minerals, Landforms, Gamebirds, Weather.

Johnson, J. - The Heritage of Our Maine Wildflowers - Courier - 1977

Knobel, E. - Field Guide to Grasses, Sedges and Rushes of the U.S. - Dover (1977)

Maine Coastal Inventory - Maine State Planning Office - (resource maps)

Maine Dept. of Inland Fisheries & Wildlife publications (various subjects)

Massachussetts Audubon - The Curious Naturalist" magazine (various habitats) 1973-'74

Martin, Zim, Nelson - American Wildlife Plants - A Guide to Wildlife Food Habits - Dover. 1951

Merryspring Foundation - P.O. Box 893. Camden. (pamphlets on plants at Merryspring)

Miller, Dorcas - Nature Lover's Guide to the Maine Coast. East Woods. 1978

National Wildlife Federation - 1412. 16th St. N.W. Wash. DC. 20036. pamphlets on habitats.

New York State Dept. of Environmental Conservation. Division of Educational Services.

Northern New England Marine Education Projects (NNMEP) Me. St. Dept. of Marine Resources

Oliver, J. ed. - The Living World - Warwick Press. 1976

Peterson, R.T. & Mckenny, M. - A Field Guide to Wildflowers - Houghton. Mifflin Co. 1968

Pettingill, O.S. - Enjoying Maine Birds - Maine Audubon Soc. 1972

Symonds, G.W.D. - The Shrub Identification Book - Morrow 1963
The Tree Identification Book - Morrow. 1958

Time and Tide - Resource Conservation & Development Project - Program of Action. 1974. (Waldoboro)

Edey, Maitland, - The North East Coast - American Wilderness Series. Time-Life. 1972

Weather

Feller-Roth, Barbara - Maine Report column. Maine Times newspaper

Gribell, Bill - Around the Harbor - column - Camden Herald newpaper

Ludlum, David - The Country Journal New England Weatherbook - H-Mifflin 1976

Maine Agricultural Extension Station - Maine Rain - Bulletin 715 1975 UMO

- Freezes in Maine Bulletin 679 1969 UMO

Minnaert, M. - Light + Colour - Dover 1954

Whelpley, Donald A. - Weather, Water + Boating - Cornell Mtn. Press. 1961

Geology

Bickel, C.E - Bedrock Geology of the Belfast Quadrangle, Me - Phd Thesis - Harvard (unpubl.)

Buckman, H.O. + Brady, N.C. - The Nature and Properties of Soils - MacMillan 1969

Dietz, R.S. - Geosynclines, Mountains + Continent Building 1970] in "Continents Adrift - Readings

" + Holden, J.C. The Breakup of Pangea 1972] from Scientific American." WH Freeman '72

Maine Geological Survey. Dept. of Conservation. Augusta. bedrock maps - surficial

Osberg, P.H. + Guidotti, C.V. - The geology of the Camden-Rockport Area - Oct 1974

p 48.55. NEIGC (New England Intercollegiate Geological Conf.

Rourke, R., Ferwerda, J., LaFlamme, K. - The Soils of Maine - UMO 1978

Holyoke, V., Arno, J., Rourk, R. - Soil Resources of Maine - Coop. Ext Serv. UMO

Salt Water

Bigelow + Schroeder - Fishes of the Gulf of Maine - U.S. gov. Print Off. 1953, Wood's Hole Oceanographic Inst., Mus. of Comp. Zoo., Harvard Univ

Carson, Rachel, - The Edge of the Sea - H-Miff. Co. 1979 (1955)

Gosner, Kenneth L. - A Field Guide to the Atlantic Seashore - Houghton Mifflin Co. 1978

Me. Dept. of Marine Resources. various publications on commercial fishing.

see "Buyer's Guide for Maine Seafoods"

Meinboth, N.A., - Audubon Society Field guide to N Am. Seashore Creatures - Knopf. 1981

New England Marine Education Services. (various materials) Box 4, Newtonville Mass. 02160

Ramsdell, Cathy. - Whales of the Gulf of Maine - Allied Whale. College of the Atlantic. Bar Harbor Me.

Robbins, S + Yentsch, C - The Sea is All About Us - Peabody Mus. of Salem and Cape Ann Soc. for Marine Studies - 1973

BIBLIOGRAPHY

S.E. New England Marine Environments _ U. of Mass. Coop. Extensions (field guide sheets on Tidal Flats, Rocky & Man Made Shores etc)

Teal, J. & M., Life & Death of the Salt Marsh _ Little & Brown - 1969

Ursin, M._Life in & around the Salt Marshes - Crowell 1972

Fresh Water

Dietz, L. & Tolman, E. _ A Special Place, The Oyster River Bog - Camden Herald. 1984

Environmental Protection Agency - New England Wetlands, Plant Identification & Protective Laws May 1981

Everhart, W.H. - Fishes of Maine - Me. Fish & Wildlife . Summer. 1976

Gorvet, J - Life in Ponds - American Heritage 1970

Hotchkiss, Neil_Common Marsh, Underwater & Floating Leaf Plants of U.S. & Canada_Dover 1967

Russel, F. _Watchers at the Pond - Time-Life 1961

Ursin, M._Life in & around Fresh water Wetlands_ Crowell. 1975

Native American

Chase, M. - Field guide to Edible & Useful Wild Plants _ Nature Study Aids NASCO 1964

Day, M & Whitmore, C _Ripe Berry Moon - Tidegrass Pr. Peak's Isl. Me. 1977

Densmore, F._How Indians Use Wild Plants for Food, Medicine & Crafts _ Dover (1925) 1977

Eastman, C.A_Indian Scout Crafts & Lore _(1914) Dover

Eckstrom, F.H. - Indian Place Names of the Penobscot Valley & Maine Coast - Maine Studies 1978

Favour, Edith _First Families, Woodland People of Maine & the Canadian Maritimes - Me. Dept. of Education & Cultural Services 1975

Maine Studies Curriculum Project - Maine Dirigo "I Lead" - Down East 1980

Project Indian Pride _ Bilingual Materials. Box 412 River Rd Calais 04619

Russel, H.S. _ Indian New England Before the Mayflower _ Univ. Press of New England. Hanover N.H. 1980

Seton, E.T._Two Little Savages _Doubleday 1925 (Dover)

Smith, N._Penobscot Traditions _ 1954. booklet at Maine State Library. Augusta.

Speck, F. _ Penobscot Man - Octogon N.Y 1940

Sturdevant, W.C. ed. - Hand book of North American Indians Vol 15. "North East." Smithsonian 1978

Wilbur, C.K. The New England Indians Global Pequot Press. Chester Conn. 1978

European

Back Door magazine (C-R High School - teacher: Peter Hope) 1979-

Camden Herald - Camden-Rockport Bicentennial 1769-1969 (booklet)
"Looking Back" - newspaper column.

Carlson, S. Rockport, Camden - Lincolnville 1776-1976 The Town Crier. 1975

Clifford, H.B. Maine and Her People. Bond Wheelwright Co. Freeport 1968

Dietz, L. The Camden Hills, an Informal History of the Camden Rockport Region Camden Herald. 1966 1947

Kellog. Elijah. The Elm Island Series. (out of print)

Locke, J.L. History of Camden 1859

Robinson, History of Camden & Rockport 1907 (reprinted by Camden Herald Pub. Co.)

Sloane, Eric Diary of an Early American Boy. Ballantine 1965
A Museum of Early American Tools. " 1964
A Reverence for Wood " 1965

Smith, Ray & Betty. "Camden-Rockport. A Historical Perspective" - in 200 Years of America - a View from Camden - Bicentennial publication - 1976

Wells. W. Water Power of Maine Augusta 1869 (Colby Library)

Wilder, Laura Ingalls. Little House Books

Museums

Abbe Museum of Acadia National Park. Bar Harbor (summer)

Conway House & Mary Cramer Museum. Camden (summer)

Maine State Museum. Augusta.

Matthews Museum of Maine Heritage. Union (summer)

Penobscot Marine Museum - Searsport.